Technology Interactions

Teacher's Resource Guide

Glencoe McGraw-Hill

New York, New York   Columbus, Ohio   Woodland Hills, California   Peoria Illinois

Glencoe/McGraw-Hill

*A Division of The **McGraw-Hill** Companies*

Send all inquiries to:
Glencoe/McGraw-Hill
3008 W. Willow Knolls Drive
Peoria, IL 61614

ISBN 0-02-677701-0

Printed in the United States of America

2 3 4 5 6 7 8 9 10   087   02 01 00 99

ACKNOWLEDGMENTS

The publisher gratefully acknowledges the cooperation and assistance received from many persons during the development of the *Technology Interactions Teacher's Resource Guide (TRG)*. Special recognition is given to the following persons for their contributions.

Contributing Writers

Pamela J. Brown
Technology Education Instructor
Central Middle School
Newnan, Georgia

Michael F. Crull
Technology Education Instructor
West Jay Junior High School
Dunkirk, Indiana

Carole Fletcher
Normal, Illinois

Patrick J. Gunter
Technology Education Instructor
R.P. Dawkins Middle School
Moore, South Carolina

Henry R. Harms
Industrial Technology Teacher
McBee High School
Chesterfield County, South Carolina

Jody A. James
James Editorial Consulting
Oviedo, Florida

Curtis Nelson
Industrial Technology Teacher
Washington Community High School
Washington, Illinois

Deborah Paul
Worthington, Ohio

Thomas N. Pitchford
Technology Education Teacher
Valdosta Middle School
Valdosta, Georgia

Mark Roberts
Technology Teacher
McLane Middle School
Brandon, Florida

Neal R. Swernofsky
Technology Teacher
Lincoln Orens School
Island Park, New York

Amy L. Watterson
Munster, Indiana

Composition

Jody A. James
James Editorial Consulting
Oviedo, Florida

TABLE OF CONTENTS

Overview

The Overview describes the components of the *Technology Interactions* program, which include a Student Text and a Teacher's Resource Guide (TRG). The Overview also contains a Resources list, which includes videos, CD-ROMs, textbooks, trade books, etc., that provide supplemental information suitable for use with the *Technology Interactions* program. The last section of the Overview includes correlations to the national standards in mathematics, science, and technology.

The Technology Interactions Program

THE STUDENT TEXT

Education theory has long maintained that people remember more of what they learn if they have the opportunity to apply the knowledge soon after acquiring it. The *Technology Interactions* student text, designed to be used with modular instruction, provides this opportunity. It is a hands-on, interactive learning experience that helps students apply principles and concepts as they learn them.

Features

At the beginning of each chapter, objectives and key terms help students focus on central concepts by orienting them to the purpose and main ideas of the chapter. Each chapter also has a Chapter Review section complete with a summary of major concepts, "Check Your Facts" questions, and "Critical Thinking" questions.

Other features link chapter content with other subject matter. In particular, the "Linking to" features link the technological concepts being discussed with math, science, and communication. The "Linking to the Workplace" feature helps students understand how major concepts are used in "real-world" situations in a working environment. "Fascinating Facts" provide interesting sidelights on the discussion.

Chapter Activities

Each chapter has at least two activities that allow students to apply the principles and concepts presented in the chapter. These activities supplement activities in modular programs. They are basic enough to allow students to succeed, yet they are pertinent to the subject matter, allowing students to make a connection easily between the activity and the chapter content.

THE TEACHER'S RESOURCE GUIDE

The Teacher's Resource Guide (TRG) complements the *Technology Interactions* student text in several ways. It provides information teachers can use to plan lessons and modules, including lists of resources that can be used to augment their teaching materials and correlations to national standards in math, science, and technology.

Lab Development and Safety Tips

For teachers and administrators who are new to modular instruction, the TRG includes an article called "Starting, Financing, and Managing a Modular Technology Program." This article provides practical advice and tips for getting started, as well as for managing a modular classroom on an ongoing basis. A companion article offers suggestions for assessing student achievements in the modular environment.

The full-featured section on safety includes a discussion of safety in a modular laboratory. This section also contains reproducible handouts on various safety issues, as well as safety posters that can be reproduced and posted in the technology laboratory.

Lesson Plans

The TRG provides a lesson plan for every chapter in the student text. Each lesson plan includes the chapter objectives for ready reference, as well as suggestions for tying the chapter content to students' previous knowledge. The "Teach" portion of the lesson plans offers teaching suggestions and provides answers to the "Check Your Facts" questions and "Linking to Mathematics" items in the student text. Finally, each lesson plan includes reteaching and assessment suggestions and tips for the "Apply What You've Learned" activity.

Career Activities and Assessment

The TRG includes career activities for each chapter. These activities encourage students to think about and possibly pursue career possibilities in which they may be interested.

Finally, a review and test is provided for each chapter in the student text. Answer keys for the reviews, tests, and career activities are provided at the end of the TRG.

Resources

The following books and other publications contain information related to topics that are covered in the *Technology Interactions* textbook. Use them to expand and enhance your lessons. Many of these resources are referenced in the Lesson Plans, which begin on page 61.

Brusic, Sharon; Fales, James; and Kuetemeyer, Vincent. *Technology Today and Tomorrow*. Peoria, IL: Glencoe/McGraw-Hill, 1999.
This book is an excellent resource for information about manufacturing, construction, communication, transportation, and bio-related technologies.

Gilchrist, Peter. *Boeing 747-400*. Osceola, WI: Motorbooks International Publishers, 1998.
This four-color book has many pictures of the 747 and the different ways it can be configured.

Hawkes, Nigel. *Structures: The Way Things Are Built*. New York: Collier Books, 1993.
This book is an excellent source of information for the aspiring architect or for the person who just wants to know more about how structures are built.

Levy, Matthys and Salvadori, Mario. *Why Buildings Fall Down*. New York: W. W. Norton & Company, Inc., 1992.
This explains why several major disasters occurred and what caused the buildings involved in these disasters to collapse.

Macaulay, David (illustrator) and Ardley, Neil. *The New Way Things Work*. Boston: Houghton Mifflin Co., 1998.
This very popular book is a great resource to include in your library.

Mighty Machines-Airplane. New York: Dorling Kindersley, 1995.
This is an informative, elementary level book for someone wanting a brief overview of the airplane and the machines that operate at an airport.

Nelson, Peter. *Treehouses*. Boston: Houghton Mifflin, 1994.
This book takes a serious approach to building a tree house. Among the excellent pictures in this four-color book are many that show tree houses under construction.

Physical Science Interactive CD-ROM. Westerville, OH: Glencoe/McGraw-Hill, 1999.
This CD-ROM demonstrates physics concepts using live video, articles, games, and animations in a student-oriented way.

Physical Science Interactive Videodiscs. Westerville, OH: Glencoe/McGraw-Hill, 1999.
These videodiscs show how physics concepts apply to the real world.

Salvadori, Mario. *Why Buildings Stand Up: The Strength of Architecture*. New York: W. W. Norton & Company, Inc., 1990.
Perhaps the best of the "buildings" books, this text explains the key ideas of all types of structures. It is especially good for bridge construction.

Science Interactions 4. Westerville, OH: Glencoe/McGraw-Hill, 1998.
This book has tremendous coverage of the environment and ecosystems, global warming, construction of shelters, electricity and electronics, and flight.

Stevenson, Neil. *Architecture*. New York: Dorling Kindersley, 1997.
This book includes beautiful pictures of many types of architecture from different cultures.

Upton, Jim. *Boeing 777*. North Branch, MN: Specialty Press, 1998.
This well-illustrated book gives a thorough explanation of the various systems of the Boeing 777 and all aspects of the plane's design.

Visual Dictionary of Flight. New York: Dorling Kindersley, 1992.
This well-illustrated book gives an outstanding presentation of all elements of flight.

Visual Dictionary of Physics. New York: Dorling Kindersley, 1995.
This book shows many interesting applications of physics in our everyday lives.

Correlations to NCTM Standards

(National Council of Teachers of Mathematics)

Standard	Ch. 1	Ch. 2	Ch. 3	Ch. 4
1. Mathematics as Problem Solving	Linking to Mathematics			Linking to Mathematics
2. Mathematics as Communication	Linking to Mathematics/Both activities	Linking to Mathematics/All activities	Entire chapter	Linking to Mathematics
3. Mathematics and Reasoning				
4. Mathematical Connections	Linking to Mathematics/Both activities	Linking to Mathematics/All activities	Entire chapter	Linking to Mathematics
5. Numbers and Number Relationships		Design & Build a Spreadsheet	CAD Advantages/ Cartesian Coordinate System/Linking to Mathematics	
6. Number Systems and Number Theory		Design & Build a Spreadsheet	CAD Advantages/ Cartesian Coordinate System/Linking to Mathematics	
7. Computation and Estimation	Linking to Mathematics	All activities	Design & Build a Site Plan	Linking to Mathematics
8. Patterns and Functions				
9. Algebra				
10. Statistics				
11. Probability				
12. Geometry	Design & Build a Profile Map of an Ocean Floor		Entire chapter	
13. Measurement	Both activities	All activities	Design & Build a Site Plan	Linking to Mathematics

(continued next page)

Correlations to NCTM Standards (continued)

Standard	Ch. 5	Ch. 6	Ch. 7	Ch. 8
1. Mathematics as Problem Solving	Linking to Mathematics	Linking to Mathematics	Linking to Mathematics	Linking to Mathematics
2. Mathematics as Communication	Linking to Mathematics	Linking to Mathematics	Linking to Mathematics	Linking to Mathematics/ Linking to Communication
3. Mathematics and Reasoning				
4. Mathematical Connections	Linking to Mathematics	Linking to Mathematics	Linking to Mathematics	Linking to Mathematics/ Linking to Communication
5. Numbers and Number Relationships				Linking to Mathematics
6. Number Systems and Number Theory				Linking to Mathematics
7. Computation and Estimation	Linking to Mathematics	Linking to Mathematics	Linking to Mathematics	Linking to Mathematics
8. Patterns and Functions				
9. Algebra				
10. Statistics				
11. Probability				
12. Geometry				
13. Measurement	Design & Build a Zoetrope		Radio Broadcasting	Linking to Mathematics

(continued next page)

TECHNOLOGY INTERACTIONS Teacher's Resource Guide

Correlations to NCTM Standards (continued)

Standard	Ch. 9	Ch. 10	Ch. 11	Ch. 12
1. Mathematics as Problem Solving	Linking to Mathematics	Linking to Mathematics	Linking to Mathematics	Hydraulic Systems/Linking to Science/Linking to Mathematics
2. Mathematics as Communication	Linking to Mathematics/Design & Build a Small Structure	Fascinating Facts (1st)/Linking to Mathematics/Design & Build a Propeller	Linking to Mathematics/All activities	Pressure/Hydraulic Systems/Linking to Science/Linking to Mathematics
3. Mathematics and Reasoning		Design & Build a Propeller		
4. Mathematical Connections	Linking to Mathematics/Design & Build a Small Structure	Linking to Mathematics/Design & Build a Propeller	Linking to Mathematics/All activities	Pressure/Hydraulic Systems/Linking to Science/Linking to Mathematics
5. Numbers and Number Relationships	Linking to Mathematics		Linking to Mathematics	Linking to Science/Linking to Mathematics
6. Number Systems and Number Theory	Linking to Mathematics/Design & Build a Small Structure		Linking to Mathematics	Linking to Science/Linking to Mathematics
7. Computation and Estimation	Linking to Mathematics/Design & Build a Small Structure	Linking to Mathematics	Linking to Mathematics	Hydraulic Systems/Linking to Science/Linking to Mathematics
8. Patterns and Functions		Design & Build a Propeller		
9. Algebra		Linking to Mathematics	Linking to Mathematics	Pressure/Hydraulic Systems/Linking to Science/Linking to Mathematics
10. Statistics				
11. Probability				
12. Geometry				Linking to Mathematics
13. Measurement	Linking to Mathematics/Design & Build a Small Structure	Fascinating Facts (1st)/Linking to Mathematics/All activities	Linking to Mathematics/Design & Build a Model Maglev System/Design & Build a Catamaran	Hydraulic Systems/Linking to Science/Linking to Mathematics

(continued next page)

Correlations to NCTM Standards (continued)

Standard	Ch. 13	Ch. 14	Ch. 15	Ch. 16
1. Mathematics as Problem Solving	Linking to Mathematics	Linking to Mathematics	Linking to Mathematics	Linking to Mathematics
2. Mathematics as Communication	Linking to Mathematics	Mechanization/Linking to Mathematics/Impacts	Linking to Mathematics Ohm's Law/Uses and Types of Transistors	CNC/Linking to Mathematics/Cartesian Coordinates/Codes
3. Mathematics and Reasoning				
4. Mathematical Connections	Linking to Mathematics	Mechanization/Linking to Mathematics/Impacts/Design & Build a Casein Glue Manufacturing System	Linking to Mathematics/Uses and Types of Transistors	CNC/Linking to Mathematics/Cartesian Coordinates/Codes/Design & Build CNC Coordinates
5. Numbers and Number Relationships		Linking to Mathematics/Impacts	Linking to Mathematics	Linking to Mathematics
6. Number Systems and Number Theory		Linking to Mathematics	Linking to Mathematics/Uses and Types of Transistors	Linking to Mathematics
7. Computation and Estimation	Linking to Mathematics	Linking to Mathematics/Design & Build a Casein Glue Manufacturing System	Linking to Mathematics	Linking to Mathematics
8. Patterns and Functions	Linking to Mathematics			
9. Algebra			Ohm's Law/Linking to Mathematics	
10. Statistics		Mechanization/Impacts		
11. Probability				
12. Geometry				CNC/Cartesian Coordinates/Codes/Design & Build CNC Coordinates
13. Measurement	Linking to Science	Linking to Mathematics/Design & Build a Casein Glue Manufacturing System		Linking to Science/Linking to Mathematics/Design & Build CNC Coordinates

(continued next page)

TECHNOLOGY INTERACTIONS Teacher's Resource Guide

Correlations to NCTM Standards (continued)

Standard	Ch. 17	Ch. 18	Ch. 19	Ch. 20
1. Mathematics as Problem Solving	Linking to Mathematics	Linking to Mathematics	Linking to Mathematics	Newton's Second Law of Motion/ Work/Power/Linking to Mathematics
2. Mathematics as Communication	Linking to Mathematics/ Binary Code	Linking to Mathematics/ Design & Build a Light-Carrying Device	Linking to Mathematics/A Shelf for a School Locker	Gravity/Newton's Second Law of Motion/Work/ Power/Linking to Mathematics
3. Mathematics and Reasoning				Newton's Second Law of Motion
4. Mathematical Connections	Linking to Mathematics/ Binary Code	Linking to Mathematics/ Design & Build a Light-Carrying Device	Linking to Mathematics/A Shelf for a School Locker	Newton's Second Law of Motion/ Linking to Mathematics
5. Numbers and Number Relationships	Linking to Mathematics	Linking to Mathematics		Gravity/Work
6. Number Systems and Number Theory	Linking to Mathematics/ Binary Code	Linking to Mathematics		Work
7. Computation and Estimation	Linking to Mathematics	Linking to Mathematics	Linking to Mathematics	Work/Power/ Linking to Mathematics
8. Patterns and Functions				Newton's Second Law of Motion
9. Algebra	Linking to Mathematics			Newton's Second Law of Motion/ Work/Power
10. Statistics				
11. Probability				
12. Geometry	Linking to Mathematics	Design & Build a Light-Carrying Device	Linking to Mathematics	
13. Measurement	Linking to Mathematics	Linking to Mathematics/ Design & Build a Light-Carrying Device	Linking to Mathematics/A Shelf for a School Locker	Work/Power/ Linking to Mathematics/Design & Build a Crane/ Design & Build a "Reaction" Rocket Racer

Correlations to Science Education Standards

Standard	Ch. 1	Ch. 2	Ch. 3	Ch. 4
A. Science as Inquiry		Linking to Science		
B. Physical Science	Linking to Science/ Design & Build a Lifting Device		Linking to Science	Linking to Science
C. Life Science				
D. Earth and Space Science	Design & Build a Profile Map of an Ocean Floor			
E. Science and Technology	Impacts/Critical Thinking/All activities/Linking to the Workplace	Entire chapter	All activities	Introduction/ Fascinating Facts/ All activities
F. Science in Personal and Social Perspectives	Throughout chapter	The Design Process/ Identify the Need/ Fascinating Facts (both)	Introduction/ CAD Advantages/ The Future/All activities	Introduction/ Fascinating Facts
G. History and Nature of Science	Career profiles	Throughout chapter	Career profiles	Introduction/ Fascinating Facts
H. Unifying Concepts and Processes	Systems in Technology/ Systems and Subsystems/ Critical Thinking/ Design & Build a Lifting Device/ Design & Build a Profile Map of an Ocean Floor	Modeling Techniques/ Implement the Solution/Using the Design Process/ All activities	Two-Dimensional and Three- Dimensional CAD	

(continued next page)

TECHNOLOGY INTERACTIONS Teacher's Resource Guide

Correlations to Science Education Standards (continued)

Standard	Ch. 5	Ch. 6	Ch. 7	Ch. 8
A. Science as Inquiry				
B. Physical Science			Throughout chapter	Metals/Linking to Science/ Fascinating Facts
C. Life Science	What Is Animation?/ Linking to Science		Electronic Communication/ Linking to Science	Wood
D. Earth and Space Science				
E. Science and Technology	Computer Animation/Linking to Mathematics/ Impacts/The Future/All activities	Impacts/The Future/All Activities	Fascinating Facts (1st)/Impacts of Television/Impacts of Multimedia/ All activities	Throughout chapter
F. Science in Personal and Social Perspectives	Introduction/ Computer Animation/Linking to Mathematics/ Impacts/The Future/Career profiles	Throughout chapter	Throughout chapter	Throughout chapter
G. History and Nature of Science	Career profiles	What Is the Internet?/Building the Internet	Fascinating Facts (1st)/Career profiles	Fascinating Facts/ Career profiles
H. Unifying Concepts and Processes				

(continued next page)

Correlations to Science Education Standards (continued)

Standard	Ch. 9	Ch. 10	Ch. 11	Ch. 12
A. Science as Inquiry				
B. Physical Science	Throughout chapter	Entire chapter	Throughout chapter	Fluid Science/ Pressure/ Hydraulic Systems/ Linking to Science/ Critical Thinking
C. Life Science				
D. Earth and Space Science				
E. Science and Technology	Impacts/Both activities	Newton's Three Laws/Fascinating Facts (2nd & 4th) Aerodynamics/All activities	Throughout chapter	Pressure/ Pneumatic Systems/The Future of Fluid Power/All activities
F. Science in Personal and Social Perspectives	What Is a Structure?/Impacts/ The Future/Career profiles	Newton's Three Laws/Fascinating Facts (2nd & 4th)	Throughout chapter	Introduction/ Pressure/Fluid Power System Safety/Linking to the Workplace/ Career profiles
G. History and Nature of Science	Linking to the Workplace/ Career profiles	Newton's Three Laws/Fascinating Facts (2nd & 4th)	Throughout chapter	Pressure/Linking to the Workplace/ Career profiles
H. Unifying Concepts and Processes	Throughout chapter	Throughout chapter	Throughout chapter	

(continued next page)

Correlations to Science Education Standards (continued)

Standard	Ch. 13	Ch. 14	Ch. 15	Ch. 16
A. Science as Inquiry				
B. Physical Science		Plant Growth/ Design & Build a Casein Glue Manufacturing System	Entire chapter	Computer Modeling/Linking to Science
C. Life Science	Entire chapter	Entire chapter		
D. Earth and Space Science				
E. Science and Technology	Fascinating Facts (3rd & 4th)/ Materials/ Questionable Developments/ Critical Thinking/ All activities	Fascinating Facts (all)/Hydroponics/ Impacts/Critical Thinking/All activities/Career profiles	Generators/ Semiconductors/ Both activities/ Career profiles	Throughout chapter
F. Science in Personal and Social Perspectives	Throughout chapter	Throughout chapter	Introduction/ Generators/ Semiconductors/ Linking to the Workplace/Career profiles	Computers and Product Design/ Flexible Manufacturing System (FMS)/ Critical Thinking/ Career profiles
G. History and Nature of Science	Fascinating Facts (2nd)/Career profiles		Generators/ Semiconductors/ Career profiles	Part Design/ Career profiles
H. Unifying Concepts and Processes	Ergonomics/ Environment Design		Electronic Systems/ Critical Thinking	Computer Modeling/Linking to Science/Design & Build a Product Concept

(continued next page)

Correlations to Science Education Standards (continued)

Standard	Ch. 17	Ch. 18	Ch. 19	Ch. 20
A. Science as Inquiry				
B. Physical Science		Entire chapter	Using the Engineering Process: A Case Study/Linking to Science/Identify the Need/Gather Information/Implement the Solution/Critical Thinking	Entire chapter
C. Life Science	Throughout chapter	Fascinating Facts (1st)		
D. Earth and Space Science		Fascinating Facts (2nd & 3rd)		Gravity/Gravitational Force and Technology
E. Science and Technology	Introduction/Early Mechanisms Punch Cards and Computers/Impacts/Both activities/Career profiles	Introduction/Lasers/Fascinating Facts (2nd)/Communication/All activities/Career profiles	Entire chapter	Throughout chapter
F. Science in Personal and Social Perspectives	Throughout chapter	Laser Safety/Communication/Medicine/the Future/Linking to the Workplace/Career profiles	What Is Engineering?/"Classic Engineering"/A New Generation of Engineering/Fascinating Facts (2nd)/The Future/Career profiles	Throughout chapter
G. History and Nature of Science	Introduction/Early Mechanisms/Punch Cards and Computers/Career profiles	Lasers/Fascinating Facts (2nd)/Communication/Career profiles	Fascinating Facts (2nd)/Using the Engineering Process: A Case Study/Linking to Science/Career profiles	Introduction/Newton's Laws of Motion/Linking to Mathematics/Career profiles
H. Unifying Concepts and Processes	Feedback Control		Implement the Solution (both)	

Correlations to Standards for Technology Education (Draft)

Standard	Ch. 1	Ch. 2	Ch. 3	Ch. 4
1. Designing and Developing Technological Systems	Both activities	Entire chapter	All activities	All activities
2. Determining and Controlling the Behavior of Technological Systems	Systems in Technology/ Systems and Subsystems/ Critical Thinking			
3. Utilizing Technological Tools, Resources, and Systems	Both activities	Modeling Techniques/Using the Design Process/ All activities	Entire chapter	Entire chapter
4. Assessing the Impacts and Consequences of Technological Systems	Tools of Technology/ Activities of Technology/ Impacts/Critical Thinking/Linking to the Workplace	Fascinating Facts (both)/Identify the Need/Critical Thinking	CAD Advantages/ The Future	Introduction/ Fascinating Facts/ The Publishing Process
5. Nature and Evolution of Technology	Throughout chapter	The Design Process/Fascinating Facts (both)/ Critical Thinking	Introduction/ CAD Advantages	Introduction/ Fascinating Facts/ The Publishing Process
6. Linkages	"Linking to" features/Career profiles	Fascinating Facts (both)/Identify the Need/"Linking to" features/Career profiles	"Linking to" features/Career profiles	"Linking to" features/Career profiles
7. Technological Concepts and Principles	Entire chapter	Entire chapter	Entire chapter	Entire chapter

(continued next page)

Correlations to Standards for Technology Education (continued)

Standard	Ch. 5	Ch. 6	Ch. 7	Ch. 8
1. Designing and Developing Technological Systems	All activities	Entire chapter	All activities	Design and Engineering/ All activities
2. Determining and Controlling the Behavior of Technological Systems				
3. Utilizing Technological Tools, Resources, and Systems	Entire chapter	Entire chapter		Throughout chapter
4. Assessing the Impacts and Consequences of Technological Systems	Introduction/ Computer Animation/Linking to Mathematics/ Impacts/The Future	Introduction/ Building the Internet/Linking to Communications/ Impacts/The Future	Impacts of Television/ Television in the Future/Impacts of Multimedia/The Future of Multimedia	Society/The Environment/ The Future
5. Nature and Evolution of Technology	Introduction/What Is Animation?/ Hand-Drawn Animation/ Computer Animation	Building the Internet/Impacts	Fascinating Facts (both)/Television	Introduction/ Fascinating Facts
6. Linkages	"Linking to" features/Career profiles	"Linking to" features/Career profiles	"Linking to" features/Career profiles	"Linking to" features/Career profiles
7. Technological Concepts and Principles	Entire chapter	Entire chapter	Entire chapter	Entire chapter

(continued next page)

TECHNOLOGY INTERACTIONS Teacher's Resource Guide

Correlations to Standards for Technology Education (continued)

Standard	Ch. 9	Ch. 10	Ch. 11	Ch. 12
1. Designing and Developing Technological Systems	Both activities	All activities	All activities	All activities
2. Determining and Controlling the Behavior of Technological Systems	Building Is a System/Building a Residential Structure/Plan Preparation		Systems in Transportation/ Common Elements	
3. Utilizing Technological Tools, Resources, and Systems	Structural Materials/ Fascinating Facts (3rd)/Finishing the Structure/Critical Thinking	All activities	All activities	All activities
4. Assessing the Impacts and Consequences of Technological Systems	What Is a Structure?/ Impacts/The Future/Critical Thinking	Fascinating Facts (2nd)/A Closer Look	Powering Rail Systems/Rail Transportation Today/Maglev/ Powering Vessels/ Impacts/Critical Thinking	Throughout chapter
5. Nature and Evolution of Technology	What Is a Structure?	Newton's Three Laws/Fascinating Facts (all)/Critical Thinking	Land Transportation/ Rail Transportation/ Powering Rail Systems/Rail Transportation Today/Marine Transportation/ Powering Vessels	Introduction/ Fascinating Facts (both)/Pressure
6. Linkages	"Linking to" features/Career profiles	"Linking to" features/Career profiles	"Linking to" Features/Career profiles	Throughout chapter
7. Technological Concepts and Principles	Entire chapter	Entire chapter	Entire chapter	Entire chapter

(continued next page)

Correlations to Standards for Technology Education (continued)

Standard	Ch. 13	Ch. 14	Ch. 15	Ch. 16
1. Designing and Developing Technological Systems	Physical Enhancements/ All activities/ Ergonomics/ Environment Design	All activities	Both activities	Introduction/Computers and Product Design/Computer Modeling/Part Design/CAD/ CAM/All activities
2. Determining and Controlling the Behavior of Technological Systems			Electronic Systems/ Critical Thinking	
3. Utilizing Technological Tools, Resources, and Systems	Materials/Linking to Communication/ All activities	All activities	Both activities	Throughout chapter
4. Assessing the Impacts and Consequences of Technological Systems	Throughout chapter	Throughout chapter	Introduction/ Linking to Communication/ Semiconductors/ Linking to the Workplace	Computers and Product Design/ Fascinating Facts (1st)/CAD/CAM/ Flexible Manufacturing System (FMS)/Critical Thinking
5. Nature and Evolution of Technology	Fascinating Facts (all)/Information/ Health Care Technology/Prevention of Disease/ Questionable Developments	Fascinating Facts (1st & 3rd) Mechanization/ Impacts	Introduction/ Generators/ Semiconductors/ Linking to the Workplace	Computers and Product Design/ Fascinating Facts (both)/Computer Numerical Control/ CNC Data Input
6. Linkages	"Linking to" features/Career profiles	Agriculture and Environmental Technologies/ Mechanization/ Bioprocessing and the Environment/ "Linking to" features/Career profiles	"Linking to" features/Career profiles	"Linking to" features/Career profiles
7. Technological Concepts and Principles	Entire chapter	Entire chapter	Entire chapter	Entire chapter

(continued next page)

TECHNOLOGY INTERACTIONS Teacher's Resource Guide

Correlations to Standards for Technology Education (continued)

Standard	Ch. 17	Ch. 18	Ch. 19	Ch. 20
1. Designing and Developing Technological Systems	Both activities	All activities	Entire chapter	All activities
2. Determining and Controlling the Behavior of Technological Systems	Feedback Control			
3. Utilizing Technological Tools, Resources, and Systems	Both activities	All activities	All activities	All activities
4. Assessing the Impacts and Consequences of Technological Systems	Throughout chapter	Lasers/ Communication/ Medicine	What Is Engineering?/ "Classic Engineering" A New Generation of Engineering/ Impacts/The Future/Career profiles	
5. Nature and Evolution of Technology	Throughout chapter	Introduction/ Lasers/Fascinating Facts (2nd)/ Communication	Fascinating Facts (both)/"Classic Engineering"	Introduction/ Newton's Laws of Motion/Linking to Mathematics
6. Linkages	Throughout chapter	Fascinating Facts (1st)/"Linking to" features/Career profiles	Throughout chapter	"Linking to" features/Career profiles
7. Technological Concepts and Principles	Entire chapter	Entire chapter	Entire chapter	Entire chapter

Program Development

This part includes an article on how to start, finance, and manage a modular technology program. It also includes an article about assessment techniques for modular classes. The last item in the Program Development part of this TRG is a safety section that includes reproducible pages that you can use as handouts or posters in the classroom.

Starting, Financing, and Managing a Modular Technology Program

A modular technology education (MTE) program utilizes a teaching system in which the classroom is divided into modular learning stations, each populated by a team of two students. Student teams rotate through a series of self-directed instructional units. Most teachers find that 10-day units work well.

In an MTE program, students take an active role in the learning process and gain practical knowledge through hands-on activities. Working with text, videotapes, multimedia computer software, the Internet, and first-hand laboratory experiments, students learn theories, concepts, and practical applications that provide a background in the technology applied in today's high-tech global workplace.

STARTING A MODULAR TECHNOLOGY EDUCATION PROGRAM

The first step in starting an MTE program is planning. A good plan is essential in creating a successful program. The best approach to planning the program is to use teamwork. Use as many human resources as possible to get the job completed efficiently. Forming a planning committee to assist in completing the plan is a good method to use. Include students, parents, teachers, secondary and post-secondary school leaders, community organization leaders, and business and industry leaders on the committee. After the committee has formed, you can begin to develop an effective action plan. A usable plan generally includes the following elements:

- curriculum development
- facility and laboratory layout
- equipment
- funding

It is important to realize that the change to a modular technology education program cannot be an overnight change; it should be a continual evolution of the program. This is merely an extension of the idea that education is a dynamic field, not a static one. It changes constantly as the technologies around us change.

Teacher and Administration Buy-In

An important step in implementing a modular technology education laboratory is to encourage the teacher and administration of the school to "buy into" the concept and idea. Neither should feel that the program is being forced upon them. When this change is forced upon either the teacher or the administration, the program begins with a stumbling block that can lead to failure. For successful implementation, both the teacher and the administration must understand the concept and have a positive attitude about the program. They must also understand the changes that need to take place to implement the program.

The Teacher As Facilitator

One of the major changes is that the teacher must become a facilitator of learning instead of a fountain of knowledge to be dispersed equally to all students. With the modular delivery approach, the students become responsible for and are held accountable for what they are learning. The students are not spoon-fed the information, but are allowed to investigate and explore, thus gaining knowledge as well as skill in searching for and obtaining knowledge. The role of the teacher is to provide guidance and direction to the students and to assist them as needed. Therefore, the teacher must develop a new method for teaching and must, at times, be willing to learn along with the students as they delve deeper into the subject matter.

CURRICULUM FOR A MODULAR TECHNOLOGY EDUCATION LABORATORY

Curriculum development is a crucial part of creating a functional MTE laboratory. Some teachers choose to modify an existing program and build their own modules. They use materials they already have or can easily obtain, or they may choose individual commercial modules from several different vendors to suit their needs. Other teachers prefer to purchase a "turnkey" system in which one vendor supplies all the modules to be used, as well as the expertise necessary to get the lab started. The path you choose to take depends to a large extent on your school's available resources, your experience with modular instruction, and the needs of the students.

Developing a New Curriculum

If you are responsible for writing the curriculum for each module, then plan on at least a year to develop it so that you do not have to teach students while you are still developing the curriculum. You will then need to field-test your curriculum with students.

Human Resources

Involve as many of your fellow teachers as you can in the planning stage. Because many of the modules involve applied math, science, and communication skills, expertise from teachers in these areas can be very helpful. Their knowledge adds credibility and effectiveness to the curriculum. Experience has shown that widespread involvement of school and community personnel in planning the program increases its strength, impact, and reputation.

It is also important to consult the technology curriculum coordinator in your district or state to see if you need to follow specific guidelines or requirements in developing your curriculum. Even if no firm standards exist in your district or state, curriculum coordinators can often provide valuable tips and suggestions regarding the modules you choose.

Another invaluable resource in curriculum development are area business and industry leaders. Their knowledge of the needs in the workplace are vital to your plan. Also, if you include their needs in your curriculum, they may be willing to help sponsor the program. (See "Funding" later in this article.)

Identifying Program Goals

Before you can create an effective MTE program, you must have a clear idea of exactly what you

---

CHARACTERISTICS OF MODULAR TECHNOLOGY EDUCATION

- Hands-on programs are taught using an investigative, design-and-construct, problem-solving approach.

- Real-world, action-based activities challenge students to achieve their greatest potential and to develop higher-order thinking skills.

- Students study the resources, processes, systems, and products of technology.

- The curriculum is designed to be taught in a laboratory equipped with modern technological tools and devices.

- Students learn to investigate ideas and develop research skills.

---

want to achieve and how you intend to achieve it. The planning committee should think carefully about the following issues:

- What is the overall focus for technology education within the state and/or local school system?
- Is there local or school support for a modular laboratory and the modular delivery system?
- How will the laboratory/program be funded?
- Is the curriculum already established, or will you be responsible for developing it?
- What modules are available from each vendor? Should all modules be purchased from the same source?
- What modules and subject areas are appropriate for your laboratory?

Evaluating Commercial Packages

Although buying complete module packages from vendors is generally more expensive, vendors normally provide the equipment along with supplemental items and the curriculum. This can save time and effort in starting a new MTE lab. However, you will probably need to modify the curriculum after you have used it for a while to meet the needs of your students.

Before choosing a vendor, collect literature from companies that offer MTE programs. Learn what products are available and determine the general price range. Contact schools that have MTE programs. Talk with people who have developed MTE programs. Take a tour of their labs if possible. You can learn a lot from the experiences of others.

After you have determined what packages are available, analyze each potential supplier. The following questions provide basic guidelines; you may wish to add others based on your goals.

- Does the company have a record of success in helping schools establish successful technology education programs?
- Does the company offer modular programs that coincide with what you want to teach your students?
- Are the modules reasonably priced?
- Can you purchase modules and equipment as you need (or can afford) them, or does the company impose restrictions such as minimum purchase requirements?
- Does the company make it easy and affordable to replenish consumable module supplies?
- Will the modules run on your existing computer equipment? (For example, does the company offer computer software in Macintosh or IBM-compatible versions?)
- Are module lesson plans flexible so you can change them to meet specific time requirements and customize lesson plan content to suit your individual teaching preferences?
- Are lesson plans on hard copy and disks so you can easily customize the curriculum?
- Are module setup instructions complete and easy to follow, or are you required to purchase high-priced training or pay installation fees?
- Is the management system designed to be implemented easily by teachers without prior technical training and experience?
- Is the management system supplied as an added benefit, or does it come at an extra cost to the module package?
- Is competent technical assistance offered free of charge via an easily accessible 800 number?
- Are purchases offered on a "90-day Satisfaction Guaranteed" basis?

After the committee has decided which vendor is best qualified to meet your modular technology education needs, ask the vendor to help you put the finishing touches on your plan. You might be surprised at how much the vendor can help in developing your program.

Building Your Own Program

If the committee decides to build and tailor a modular program to meet your school's needs, the first step is still to develop your program goals. You will also need to define your curriculum more specifically to get a realistic idea of the cost and effort involved in implementation. After you have a basic idea of what you want to accomplish, list resources you already have that can be adjusted to fit into a modular framework. Many schools already have a more traditional type of laboratory. As you look into different kinds of modular stations, think about how you can use these current resources in the modular lab.

Modifying an Existing Curriculum

If the curriculum already exists, you may need to purchase only the equipment, rather than entire packaged modules. However, do not forget about supplemental equipment and supplies such as videos, textbooks, and other small items.

Whether you buy a complete package or modify an existing program to create the MTE lab, modification is an ongoing process. In fact, major modifications to the lab may not begin until the lab has been functioning for two to three years. During this time, you can discover what does and does not work with your students. The proper and total implementation of an MTE program generally takes between three and five years. It takes this amount of time to become comfortable with the program and get the kinks ironed out. Patience and organization are keys to implementing a modular technology education program.

> *The modular education movement assures hands-on learning and the opportunity for technology education teachers to manage students in multiple activity/technology labs effectively and efficiently.*
>
> **—Harvey Dean**

DESIGNING AND FURNISHING THE LABORATORY

One common approach to furnishing an MTE lab is to rearrange existing furniture and equipment within a classroom to fit the new modular setup. You can use tables for workstations and add inexpensive dividers to eliminate unnecessary distractions. While simple and inexpensive, this method can be very effective.

Another option is to convert an existing shop or classroom. Conversion involves the construction or purchase of workstations, electrical changes, addition of adequate lighting, and installation of storage cabinets. School district personnel or outside contractors often do this work. In some cases, a team of teachers and parents work on a volunteer basis to develop the lab.

Physical Layout of the Laboratory

Many teachers have found that a combination of classroom and laboratory space works best in a modular laboratory. The classroom area can be used to discuss common problems or to relate student work to real-world occurrences and applications. Depending on the types of modules being used and the course goals, some teachers prefer to have a separate resource, or manufacturing, area in addition to the classroom and modular areas. The setup you choose will probably depend on the space available and the specific courses you will be teaching.

When designing the lab layout, be sure to consider safety issues. Ideally, all areas of the lab should be fully visible to the teacher at all times. One teacher who needed a manufacturing area separated it from the modular area using a glass wall to maintain visibility. Another idea is to use convex mirrors in key spots to increase visibility. Also pay attention to traffic flow. During lab time, it should be easy to move and circulate through the lab to assist students.

The furniture in the lab should be durable enough to withstand many years of student use. If possible, choose furniture that can be moved and shifted as you become more familiar with the laboratory layout. You may find that a different arrangement works better; also, your needs may change over time. A wise investment now can help reduce costs later.

Modular Workstations

In selecting or designing workstations, be sure to provide sufficient space for two students to work comfortably. The work surface should be at least 8 to 10 feet wide and 24 to 36 inches deep. In considering work area size, remember that computers, VCRs, and other equipment must share this space. You'll also need two chairs or stools per workstation.

Use partitions to separate the modules. Locate panels in front and on both sides of the workstations. The partitions should rise no higher than 48 to 52 inches above the floor so that you can maintain visibility of students in the workstations.

Provide at least two electrical outlets at each work area. Call lights, which students can activate when they need assistance, are another feature to consider. A shelving unit can be added on the side of the unit for storage of module textbooks, lesson plan notebooks, and file folder storage for module worksheets. Another feature that you can add easily during the construction stage is computer network cabling.

Also consider lockable storage space to keep project materials and equipment secure. Depending on your needs and resources, this can be provided at each workstation or at a central location in the lab.

Lecture/Classroom Area

Even in a modular lab format you will need to address students as a group for orientation, taking attendance , student reports, and some types of group testing. Make plans for a seating area for these purposes. If space is not available, consider using a separate classroom located nearby.

Resource/Manufacturing Area

A separate resource or manufacturing room is recommended for power tools such as saws, drill presses, sanders, grinders, etc. The dust created by these tools can be harmful to delicate electronic equipment used in the modules. If you include such a room, remember to design it so that you can have visual contact with students at all times.

Other Facilities

Other facilities can add functionality to the MTE lab. Some, such as the teacher's station and office, are necessary for proper organization of the lab. Others are optional and can be added as needed or when funds become available.

- *Teacher's Station*—Locate the teacher's station so that you can easily see the classroom and all the workstations. Potential designs range from a simple podium to an elaborate station wired

TECHNOLOGY INTERACTIONS Teacher's Resource Guide
Copyright © Glencoe/McGraw-Hill

for lighting control, with a host computer, a file server, a PA system, and any other equipment you may need.

- *Office*—You will also need a separate, lockable office for storing scheduling and grading information, master copies of videos, software, and other valuable equipment and supplies. A telephone, fax machine, and modem are useful tools to include in the office area.
- *Storage Area*—Storage space is an important element of a well-organized modular lab. A small adjoining room with shelving units can serve this purpose. If such a room is not available, consider using lockable cabinets in the main room for storing student projects, resource materials, and other equipment.
- *Audio/Video Studio*—An enclosed room with one or more windows is ideal for audio/video modules. Provide extra electrical outlets for the extensive electronic equipment that will be needed in this area. To enhance the acoustics and sound control, cover the walls with cork, acoustic tiles, or a similar material.

Equipment

The equipment needed in the MTE lab depends on the curriculum you choose or develop and the modules you plan to include. The following equipment is typical of a well-equipped lab.

Computer Equipment

Many modules require computers and various peripherals to complete the activity assignments. Although one computer per workstation is ideal, most programs can run with one computer for every two modules. This will take some careful scheduling, and you must have portable carts for the computer equipment. Now that laptop computers are more reasonably priced, you may want to consider them instead of desktop computers for the MTE lab. Most computers now come with a fax/modem and CD-ROM already installed. This eliminates the need to purchase these peripherals separately.

Many module activities require that students print the work they perform on the computer. Laser printers are best for this purpose, but ink-jet or even dot-matrix printers are less expensive and can be used. A good ratio is one printer for every five modules.

Depending on the modules you choose to use, other computer equipment may also be useful. Examples are scanners, plotters, and video capture devices.

Videocassette Recorders (VCRs)

Videotapes are another medium often used in an MTE program. The best type of unit to purchase for the lab is a 13-inch TV/VCR combination unit. It is recommended that you have one for every two modules; store the units on portable carts for easy transport among workstations. Be sure to purchase two sets of headphones for every VCR.

Notebooks

Each student needs a notebook for storing worksheets, notes, and grading information. These should be stored in a convenient place where students can access them easily. Some teachers find that using a different color notebook for each class and labeling each notebook with a unique number helps avoid confusion among students and classes. You may also need notebooks to store master copies of lesson plans, test answer keys, and program manuals.

Audio/Video

A small PA system that is controlled from the teacher's station can help you communicate effectively with students. You may also want to invest in a laserdisc player or DVD system to give students access to many types of multimedia resources. For safety reasons, consider installing video observation cameras if the lab contains areas of obstructed visibility.

Direct Phone Line

It is strongly recommended that you install a direct phone line in the laboratory. This allows you to receive technical support on any program or equipment while working in the lab. Many school districts now install T-1 lines or other systems for fast, easy access to the Internet through a computer network system. If funding is available, another feature that can bring resources into the lab is a videophone system for teleconferencing with other educators and classes all over the world.

FUNDING

Funding must be found not only for start-up expenses for equipment and supplies, but also for ongoing expenses such as replacing consumable supplies and upgrading software and hardware when necessary. Most teachers focus only on the start-up expenses, but maintenance expenses can be equally important. This section addresses both.

Start-Up Funding

After you have completed your plan for the curriculum, lab layout, and equipment, you must garner the funds necessary to renovate the laboratory, purchase the equipment and supplies, and maintain and improve the program. Because each school differs in its fiscal management system, several options are discussed here. One or more of these options may be feasible for your school.

There are several ways to go about looking for the funds to equip a laboratory. In some states, the state legislature is willing to fund modular technology education through either full state grants or matching funds grants. These require the school system to contribute an amount equal to that provided by the state. Also check the availability of federal funds that can be used for this purpose. In some cases, the school system is able to foot the entire bill without outside help.

Grants

Grants are available from businesses, industries, foundations, and other sources if you know where to look for them and know how to write the grant proposal. Your school system, state department of education, state technology teacher organization, or the national technology teacher association (ITEA) should be able to provide you with information on grants, grant writing, and the people to contact.

Local Industries

Another way to go about attaining funds is to look to industries within your community. If you can show local business and industry that what you are teaching in the classroom is exposing students to the technologies they are applying in the workplace, they are often willing to help provide the equipment necessary to teach the students.

Never be afraid to ask companies for assistance; all they can do is say no. Some companies will provide you with cash, and others may provide you with equipment. If you cannot convince a business or industry to fund the entire program, then encourage them to fund modules that relate to their particular area of business.

You can also receive much free or almost free material from many companies just by asking for it. With these materials, you can develop your own modules and or reduce the cost of planned modules.

Partnership Plans

A partnership plan provides an interesting twist on obtaining community support. It is a structured approach that takes more time and effort, but can result in an outstanding community response. The following steps are recommended:

1. Create a "prospect list" of local organizations that might benefit from a partnership with the school. The Chamber of Commerce can assist by providing a directory of its members, as well as all of the area industries.

2. From the prospect list, create a mailing list complete with the name and title of the president or CEO of the organization. Using a word processor or database program for this task avoids the possibility of having to rekey all the information later.

3. Assign the best letter-writer on the committee to draft a one- or two-page letter explaining your interest in involving the company in a partnership to improve the educational system. Focus the letter on the benefits of your partnership plan and the quality of the modular technology education program. Then use a mail merge program and a laser printer to produce professional-looking letters and envelopes. Be sure to use good-quality paper to ensure a good impression. Personalize each letter with the top executive's name and title. Proof each letter carefully, making sure there are no spelling errors in the names or titles.

4. Mail the letters at a rate of 10 to 15 letters per week to allow yourself adequate time to follow up with telephone calls.

5. Three to five days after mailing a letter, phone the prospect and ask for a half-hour

KEYS TO SUCCESSFUL PARTNERSHIPS

- Allow companies to become educational partners for as little as $500 to $2500 (the cost of a single module)

- Invite business partners to participate actively in the development of the MTE program by joining an advisory council that helps develop the technology curriculum.

- Recognize company sponsorship by displaying engraved plaques featuring the company's name in the work area of each module workstation.

- Make regular reports to business partners relating the growth and success of the program through a technology newsletter. (In some cases, the newsletter can actually be part of the curriculum in the form of an enrichment or extra credit activity for a communication or desktop publishing module.)

- Contact the media to bring more attention to the program.

appointment to discuss the benefits of your partnership plan. The purpose of the followup call is not to sell the partnership program. Its sole purpose is to arrange a face-to-face meeting with the prospect so that he or she can hear your well-conceived action plan and be persuaded by your spirit and enthusiasm to participate.

6. Arrive promptly for your appointment, and be sure to dress appropriately. Explain your program using well-prepared presentation materials (see the following paragraph). Be polite and courteous, even if the company decides not to enter your partnership plan. Remember that this company may have good reasons for not entering the partnership at this time, but those reasons may dissolve in the future. It is always best to leave a pleasant impression.

It takes more than an interest in your particular project to convince prospective partners to invest in the MTE program. To achieve the comfort level prospects need to commit to you and your project, they must have an overall understanding of your program objectives. You must be ready to offer concise, neatly prepared presentation materials. Your materials should be well-written, to-the-point, and attractive. They should be created by people with high regard for professionalism and attention to detail. Consider including the following information in your presentation package:

- Technology Education Mission Statement/Goals

- Number of students, teachers, and administrative personnel involved in your technology education program
- Curricula now in place and curricula you want to add
- MTE laboratory floor plan
- Notable student achievements or awards in technology education
- Highlights of other successful relationships (current or past)
- Letters of support from school or district administrators
- Planning committee member credentials
- Action plan summary
- Recommended steps to initiate the partnership

Ongoing Expenses

The monies necessary to keep a program running are also important. You should ask your school for a budget that you can use each year to purchase consumable supplies and a separate one for repairs and upgrades for existing equipment. Develop a budget proposal for consumables to be used each year. Prepare similar projections for both repairs and supplies.

Another way to obtain materials for use in the lab is again to solicit from business and industry. Plastic and glass companies, cabinet shops, print shops, and telephone companies are often willing to donate scrap materials. What is scrap to them is often large enough for use within the lab. These materials also make excellent demonstration materials. If your school has a partnership plan, you also have the option of looking to business partners to help replenish consumable materials.

Responding to Community Support

It is important to be grateful—and show your gratitude—for any assistance that you receive. Remember to invite the benefactors into the laboratory to see what you are doing. This helps them see how the money was spent or how the equipment is being used. They may then be willing to contribute even more to your program.

MANAGING A MODULAR TECHNOLOGY EDUCATION LABORATORY

Managing a modular laboratory is different from managing a traditional laboratory. You must develop strategies that work effectively in the modular environment. The development of a firm set of guidelines and consequences for failure to follow these guidelines is imperative. Modular laboratories require students to take more responsibility for their learning experiences. However, students must know what is and is not expected of them before they can be held accountable for their actions. Two to three days of class orientation of rules and procedures can save you many days of headaches as the course progresses.

Discipline in an MTE lab tends to be less of a problem than in a traditional classroom setting. Students usually prefer to be working in the lab and want to keep their lab privileges. Be sure that you are firm in your expectations and consistent in applying consequences for infractions. If you say something will happen, it should happen. There are always some students who will not conform and meet the expectations, and these must be handled appropriately. One alternative is to remove the lab privileges of students who misbehave or abuse their independence. Assign these students equivalent textbook or written assignments for a week. At the end of the week, most students are glad to return to the lab and usually are unlikely to repeat the infraction.

Laboratory Organization

One of the keys of management is organization. If students are to be able to work in a module, all the necessary equipment must be there and must be working. There are no guarantees that things won't disappear; however, you can limit this with your management strategies. If you keep an inventory as a part of each module and have specific procedures to follow when items are missing or broken, you will find that fewer items disappear. Limiting the amount of movement within the lab also helps keep items where they belong.

The use of call lights is an excellent method for answering questions and monitoring the room at the same time. In this method, you move around the room and the students stay in their assigned module. You can see what is happening as you move from module to module to answer questions. The placement of trash cans and pencil sharpeners strategically around the room can also eliminate unnecessary movement.

Another good classroom management technique is the use of individual student notebooks that stay in a designated place in the lab. All work for the MTE lab is kept in the lab for use the next day. This eliminates student excuses such as "I lost it," "I left that at home," or "It's in my locker." Make the students take responsibility for the notebooks.

Grouping Students Effectively

One problem commonly encountered by teachers is that some groups of students finish their work early, while other groups may not even complete the task. To help avoid this problem, examine student ability levels in advance when possible. Then assign pairs of students that have different ability levels. This approach helps both students by allowing the students to be dependent on each other and assist each other in some way.

Special-Needs Students

Special-needs students present other challenges to modular programs. Special-needs students include those with learning disabilities, those who are physically challenged, and those who have emotional problems. You may need to consider adapting some of the lessons within modules so that the directions and worksheets are at the student's level. You may also need to adjust machines to make them more accessible to these students. In some cases, you may find other students who are willing to work with special-needs students to help them accomplish tasks.

TIPS FOR MANAGING A MODULAR TECHNOLOGY EDUCATION PROGRAM

- Be familiar with the curriculum, but do not hesitate to share information both with and from students as they learn. Allow students to show you things they have learned as they go through the modules. Viewing yourself as a facilitator, rather than a traditional teacher, makes this easier to do. Eventually, you will gain a vast knowledge about all the modules.

- Allow students to choose their lab assignments. At the end of a rotation, have one class showcase the results of the module they have completed. This advertises the station to other students and creates an incentive to choose based on students' personal interests.

- One major drawback to the modular/facilitator role is contact with the class. To increase contact, start each class period in a traditional way in the classroom area. Take attendance and talk with the students about a current event in the world of technology. Remind students that they have an open homework assignment: Pay attention to their world. It is surprisingly easy to link technological breakthroughs and world and local events to the curriculum. This can be a stimulating class discussion and provides an element of the traditional classroom for those instructors who are not ready to give up that atmosphere entirely.

- In his book *Passion for Excellence,* Tom Peters describes the effectiveness of management by walking around. It is imperative that instructors move around as much as possible in a modular setting.

- In a typical course, students produce interesting and creative items such as CO_2-powered cars, rockets, and bridges. Hold an elective fair near the end of the semester. Allow students to race and display their creations. Encourage participation by other elective classes in the school, and invite the school and student community, as well as parents, to attend. Students have a great time, and the fair is a great advertising tool. The best timing for the elective fair is usually just before students sign up for the next year's classes.

- As a behavioral incentive, consider offering a field trip once a semester to a nearby technological site of interest. The trip can be funded by students. A field trip of this sort is generally exciting and different enough to inspire good behavior in class.

- Modular programs require techniques that differ in many respects from traditional teaching techniques. If you have never managed a modular program, try to find training to help you become familiar with techniques for their effective use. Most companies that provide modules will train teachers to use them effectively. Many states have technology education coordinators who provide workshops for teacher training in modular technology and classroom management.

- Never assume that everything has been thought of and that you will not have any problems. Even with commercial modules, unexpected situations arise that require changes in plans and programs. The key to success is to be flexible and plan—as much as possible—for contingencies.

It is always a good idea to get help from the special education teachers when special-needs students are enrolled in your classes. These teachers can help by suggesting appropriate modifications and design changes to make equipment and materials safe and easier to use. In some cases, they may also provide money to purchase items to make the suggested changes.

Managing Student Absences

When students miss class, they may have a problem catching up. One way handle this is to allow them to come in before or after school and make up the work. Conscientious students will do this. There may be some things that you can send home for them to do also. However, it is important that one student's absence does not hinder other students who may be working with that student.

Another idea is to schedule occasional make-up days. During these days, the other students do enrichment or other curriculum-related activities that go along with their modules. This approach has proved effective for many teachers.

In addition to random student absences, you may need to deal with occasions when entire classes are absent. Pep rallies, school pictures, and similar activities can quickly put classes in one or two periods behind your other classes. It is difficult to maintain a manageable schedule when each class teaching period is studying a different day's lesson within the rotation schedule. Keeping all class periods on the same day of a rotation schedule will help you manage your classes more efficiently.

One solution is to insert one-day activities for the classes not affected by a schedule disruption. You can use the enrich activity included in the lesson plan for each chapter (see "Lesson Plans" in Part III of this TRG) or create other activities that relate student work to technology applications.

A FINAL NOTE

The MTE lab is not a perfect teaching tool, but it is probably as close as the school environment and budgets allow today. The students become excited about hands-on learning and doing. They can work at their own speed to practice many of today's industrial concepts and technologies. The implementation of the program is often a slow and frustrating process, but the rewards far surpass the pitfalls. Through a modular delivery system, MTE programs help develop students who are critical thinkers and problem solvers.

Modular Technology Education: A Model for Assessment

Managing a Modular Technology Education (MTE) program should include a daily assessment of students' achievements. These achievements include competencies and skills that are promoted from the first day during student orientation to the MTE program.

An excellent way to assess student accomplishments is to use the standards set by the Secretary's Commission on Achieving Necessary Skills (SCANS). The model presented here is organized and designed around the SCANS competencies and skills. You may wish to use it "as is" or alter it as necessary to fit your own technology program.

THE SECRETARY'S COMMISSION ON ACHIEVING NECESSARY SKILLS (SCANS)

The SCANS report is a management and assessment guideline that provides a firm foundation to build your program. It lists the following necessary skills as a standard to help you develop an assessment plan for your program.

Personal Skills: Students will understand how personal skill development affects their future success. They will exhibit positive attitudes, self-confidence, honesty, perseverance, self-discipline, and sociability. They will manage time and balance priorities as well as demonstrate a capacity for lifelong learning.

Interpersonal Skills: Students will understand key concepts in group dynamics, conflict resolution, and teamwork strategies. They will work cooperatively, share responsibilities, and assume leadership roles. They will demonstrate cooperative learning relationships across gender and cultural groups.

Thinking and Problem Solving Skills: Students will exhibit critical and creative thinking skills, logical reasoning, and problem solving. They will apply numerical estimation, measurement, and calculation, as appropriate. They will recognize problem situations; identify, locate, and organize needed information or data; and propose, evaluate, and select from alternative solutions.

Communication Skills: Students will understand principles of effective communication. They will communicate both orally and in writing. They will listen attentively and follow instructions, requesting clarification or additional information as needed.

Systems Competencies: Students will understand social, organizational, and technological systems. Students will monitor and correct performance and design or improve systems.

Employment Literacy: Students will understand career paths and strategies for obtaining employment within a chosen field.

Technology Literacy: Students will understand and adapt to changing technology by identifying, learning, and applying new skills to improve their performance.

ASSESSMENT PROCEDURES

Once the technology laboratory and program are up and running, you will find them easy to manage using the following management system. Evaluation becomes more objective than subjective. The point system suggested here provides students with a day-by-day record of exactly which modules they have completed and how many points they have earned. The flexible evaluation procedures offer accountability to students, parents, and administrators.

Student Grading Areas

Student grades are determined by several components. The following guideline uses a point system designed to provide a fair and accurate account of student performance. The SCANS competencies and skills developed are stressed in each area. A total of 500 points may be earned per module.

Attendance points	100
Activity points	100
Chapter review points	100
Research question points	100
Post-test points	100
Total points possible per module	500

Attendance Points

Explain to students that it is possible to earn a total of 100 attendance points for each module. Award students 10 points for each day that they attend class on time. Also award 10 points if a student misses a class if the student has an excused absence. Unexcused absences do not earn any points. Penalize students 5 points if they are late to class without a note or for any unexcused tardiness. (Note: This guideline assumes a ten-day module. The points can be adjusted for modules of other lengths.)

Activity Points

Explain to students that it is possible to earn a total of 100 activity points for each module. Award students 10 points each day for participating in the daily activities and cooperating with you and their fellow students. If a student is absent, he or she is responsible for making up these points. You may wish to provide a written make-up assignment to allow students to make up the points.

Chapter Review Points

For each module, students are responsible for completing a 20-question Chapter Review. Award students 5 points for each correct answer, for a total of 100 possible chapter review points for each module.

Chapter Test Points

For each module, students are responsible for completing a 20-question test. Award students 5 points for each correct answer, for a total of 100 possible chapter test points for each module.

Final Grade

Student grades should be determined by the total number of module points they have earned during the period divided by the total number of module points possible. For example: A student earns 450 points in one module. Divide 450 points by 500 points possible to equal a grade of 90%. Each student's final grade equals the average of the grades earned for each module the student has completed.

Authentic Assessment

Authentic assessment provides an open, flexible assessment alternative that meets the needs of all students. Authentic assessment allows you to design an assessment plan that helps students develop the skills addressed in the SCANS report. The modular technology education program's 500-point plan is flexible, and the Module Activity Performance Checklist (see p. 41) can be added to enhance the effectiveness of the plan.

Authentic assessment benefits students by:
- enabling students to demonstrate in-depth understanding.
- reflecting the thinking curriculum.
- requiring a knowledge-sharing environment.
- helping students think and reflect about what, how, and how well they are learning.
- engaging students in active, developmentally appropriate, real-world activities and tasks.
- providing the instructor with an assortment of strategies to gain comprehensive views of the abilities of students.

Some instructors do not grade students on their attendance. If you choose not to include attendance in student evaluation, you may wish to implement a 400-point grading system. Another option is to double the value of the activity points or chapter test points. Doubling the activity points is the suggested alternative because it allows you to focus on student achievement in the important skills of the SCANS.

Enrichment Activity

Each MTE Lesson Plan includes an "Enrich" suggestion that you can use as an option to provide a meaningful bonus activity to enhance student knowledge of the module subject area. This activity implements career information or other concepts not covered fully in the module (environmental and ecological impacts, social impacts, etc.). The enrich option uses existing or readily available equipment, materials, and supplies, so no new products or extra materials are required to implement the activity.

The enrich activity is designed to provide multiple levels of challenge for students of varying abilities. By providing the enrich activity as an option, you can allow average students to complete their modules successfully while you maintain the interest of faster students with supplemental

MODULE ACTIVITY PERFORMANCE CHECKLIST		
Personal Skills	Students will exhibit positive attitudes, self-confidence, honesty, perseverance, self-discipline, sociability, time management and the ability to balance priorities.	15 points
Interpersonal Skills	Students will work cooperatively, share responsibilities, assume leadership roles, and demonstrate cooperative learning relationships across gender and cultural groups.	15 points
Thinking and Problem Solving Skills	Students will exhibit critical and creative thinking skills, logical reasoning, and problem solving. They will apply numerical estimation, measurement, and calculation, as appropriate. They will recognize problem situations, identify, locate, and organize needed information, and propose, evaluate, and select from alternative solutions.	15 points
Communication Skills	Students will communicate both orally and in writing. They will listen attentively and follow instructions, requesting clarification or additional information as needed.	15 points
System Competencies	Students will understand social, organizational, and technological systems. Students will monitor and correct performance and design or improve systems.	15 points
Technological Literacy	Students will understand and adapt to changing technology by identifying, learning, and applying new skills to improve their performance.	15 points
Employment Literacy	Students will understand career paths and strategies for obtaining employment within a chosen field.	10 points
	Total	100 points

activities that match their skill level. The following list suggests several ways in which the enrich option may be implemented.

1. Assign it as an extra activity for students who finish early with their assigned modules. When you assign an enrich activity to students who finish early, decide whether to give credit for completion of the activity.
2. Allow students to complete it as a make-up activity. When you use the enrich activity as a make-up activity, you may choose to allow the student to earn back some or all points missed due to absence from the lab.
3. Assign it as an extra-credit activity. When you use the enrich activity for extra credit, you may choose to award extra points to allow students to improve their grade.

Career Activity Masters

The career activity masters provide a list of representative occupations and careers associated with the concepts and skills presented in each module. These activity masters can be used to help integrate career exploration into the module lesson plan, increasing each student's knowledge of potential career opportunities. These career-oriented activities guide students as they research the nature of the work, specific job tasks, earnings, advancement possibilities, etc., for the job titles listed. Students then analyze their findings, explaining what they would find enjoyable about the career and what they might find difficult. This process encourages students to begin thinking about their career opportunities.

Student Journal

You may wish to have students keep a journal in which they recap or summarize the day's events or concepts in their own words. This option offers reinforcement of writing and comprehension skills. Daily writing in a journal helps students focus on what, how, and how well they are learning. A self-assessment of the day's activities provides students with a method for planning daily improvement in their learning process.

Student Portfolios

Student portfolios are carefully planned collections of materials that reflect student interests, abilities, progress, and accomplishments in a given area. Portfolios serve as effective assessment tools and as dynamic instructional strategies. Unlike traditional forms of assessment, which are usually designed to evaluate isolated facts and skills, portfolios effectively, efficiently, and meaningfully capture student learning over time and across disciplines.

Portfolio assessment allows students to present a cumulative instrument in which they have the opportunity to demonstrate their successes. The educational needs of the diverse student population in today's schools can be met by a portfolio assessment plan flexible enough to provide an opportunity for all students to be heard.

Portfolio Model

The projects and product ideas for student portfolios should be developed jointly by the students and teacher according to specific models provided for each module area. The box on this page shows an example of a student portfolio for a media communications module.

Project Preparation

In preparation for each project, students must complete the following four sections.
- **Plan:** A process that helps the student design the project
- **Evidence of progress:** Evidence of a sequential process that shows the student's progress toward developing the final product

SAMPLE MEDIA COMMUNICATIONS MODULE	
Video Production	Student will produce a 3-minute video presentation. The topic must be related to a public service area staying in school, drug prevention, etc.).
Desktop Publishing	Student will produce a two-page bi-fold newsletter promoting one aspect of technology education.
Slide Presentation	Student will produce a 8-10 slide presentation to be given in any chosen academic area.
Home Page Publishing	Student will produce a home page. The home page must have the following components: Three links to other pages, an animated GIF, a link to an e-mail return address, and two graphic images.

- **Final product:** A final product that is a result of the student's work
- **Oral presentation:** An oral presentation in which the student describes the project, explains skills that were applied, and evaluates the work

SUCCESSFUL MTE ASSESSMENT

Assessment of a modular technology education laboratory is an ongoing process that must be evaluated regularly to ensure that program goals and objectives are fulfilled. This model has been tested and found to work well, but you may need to alter it to fit your school's technology program. The key to successful programs—and successful students—is the flexibility of the instructor. Technology education instructors need to be willing to adjust teaching methods and modify evaluation procedures to fulfill each student's needs. Assessment is at the top of the list of needs for educational reform, and technology educators are in the right position to take the lead in this effort. The model presented here challenges technology educators to take a firm stance and lead in the effort to make positive changes in the American educational system.

Safety: Top Priority

Safety is probably the most important topic to be covered in your class. If students are not taught the correct way to operate equipment, use materials, and think safety while in your care, they may not get that instruction anywhere else in their schooling. As a technology teacher, you have a unique opportunity to teach a skill that will never be out of date. Industry can train people to do a job, but safety and safe attitudes are learned early in life. Accidents cost everyone as insurance costs increase and product costs rise to cover the increase in insurance. The loss of work, income, and health, as well as the emotional stress stemming from injuries or deaths in a family, are also a concern of industry and society.

It is your responsibility to keep all of the students in your classes as safe as possible. You are responsible for teaching them to "Think Safety" at all times. One thing that might help you in teaching this concept is always to have your students think "What if . . . ?" Have them think ahead of their actions: "What if . . . my hand is in line with the blade and the material slips or splits?" (My hand would get cut.) "What if . . . I run in the lab and I trip or bump someone while they are working with a power tool?" (I might crack my head or cause someone to get hurt.) You could have your students create their own "What if . . ." scenarios and then share them with the class. This approach is just one way to help students to begin to "THINK SAFETY."

Safety rules should be posted around your labs for students to see and refer to regularly. These signs can be made by students or purchased commercially. Many computer programs can create these signs, such as PrintShop by Broderbund or PowerPoint by Microsoft, to mention a couple. Any graphics program should work with a little imagination. A few examples are included at the end of this section. Machine-specific rules are available from machine manufacturers (in the owner's manual) or from various sources. Some are listed later in this section.

Many schools and teachers require a perfect score on all of their safety exams. This requirement should help reduce the possibility that a student may not know the safety rules. Reproducible handouts and a safety test are provided later in this section. You may use them as presented or adapt them to fit your particular situation and teaching goals.

Require all of your students to have individual machine-specific instruction/demonstration and to demonstrate those skills successfully before you allow them to operate the machine. No student should ever be allowed to use tools—especially power tools—without first obtaining your permission.

Again, you have the opportunity of a lifetime to teach your students some critical life skills and, at the same time, enjoy yourself. Remember, you are "teaching the future, today."

Sources of Safety Information

American Society of Safety Engineers, 1800 East Oakton Street, Des Plaines, IL 60018; phone: (312)692-4121

Arrow Safety, 1007 Monitor Street, LaCrosse, WI 54603; phone: (800)284-2147 (miscellaneous safety supplies)

National Safety Council, School & College Department, 444 North Michigan Avenue, Chicago, IL 60611; phone: (312)527-4800

National Society to Prevent Blindness, Director of Eye Safety Programs, 500 East Remington Road, Schaumburg, IL 60173; phone: (312)843-2020

Occupational Safety and Health Administration (OSHA), United States Department of Labor, 200 Constitution Avenue, NW, Washington, D.C. 20216; phone: (202)523-8148

Pennsylvania Department of Education, 333 Market Street, Sixth Floor, Harrisburg, PA 17126-0333; phone (717)783-8506 (Pennsylvania Industrial Arts/Technology Education Safety Guide distributed by Pennsylvania Council of Industrial Arts/Technology Education Supervisors)

(continued next page)

Safety Rules Inc., 3727 Joan Drive, Waterloo, IA 50702; phone (319)233-0917 (safety signs and miscellaneous products)

Standards for Industrial Arts Programs, International Technology Education Association, 1914 Association Drive, Reston, VA 22091; phone: (703)860-2100

The 2000 Company, 1011 West Seventeenth Street, Costa Mesa, CA 92627

The University of Texas at Austin, Extension Instruction and Materials Center, P.O. Box 7218, Austin, TX 78713-7218; phone: (512)471-7716 (source of an expanded version of the safety test included in this section)

Safety Handout 1

Safety Is the First Priority!

One of the first rules we learned as children had nothing to do with others around us. It had to do with our own safety. Our parents or other caregivers removed objects around the home that might harm us, and they watched over us. We have been taught from early childhood to "be careful" doing this or that. Our own safety is one of the basic needs of life. We must all feel safe in our endeavors or we will fail to endeavor.

This technology course is no exception when it comes to making you feel safe. During this course, you will use tools and materials as you perform activities. In all cases, you must have a certain amount of respect for the tools and materials you are using. All are potentially dangerous if used incorrectly. There will always be certain rules you must follow to ensure your safety and the safety of those around you.

While working with the tools and materials in this course, you are required to follow all of the safety rules associated with such tools and materials. Never use any tools or materials without prior instruction and the teacher's permission. Failure to abide by all safety rules could have devastating results and may require expulsion from the labs. We all want to have a good time while learning technology, but we must all be safe in the process.

Safety starts with an attitude that says, "I will practice all safety rules at all times." The key word here is "I." You, not your neighbor or your friend, but you and only you are responsible for your actions. It only takes one time of disobeying or forgetting a safety rule for you or one or more of your classmates to be seriously injured. You or they could even be permanently disabled if you have a poor attitude about safety.

By making safety your top priority in this class, you and your classmates will develop a lifelong skill that time and technology will never overtake. A proper attitude about safety will help you become a more productive citizen and worker in whatever field of employment you choose as an adult. If we all work together in this class, we will be safe in our endeavors and we may endeavor great things.

Think Safety!

TECHNOLOGY INTERACTIONS Teacher's Resource Guide
Copyright © Glencoe/McGraw-Hill

45

Industrial Technology Education:
"Learning to Live in a Technical World"*

Dear Parent/Guardian:

The technology classes at our school are designed to give students experience with hands-on activities dealing with the work-a-day world. To accomplish the goals of the curriculum, it will be necessary for your son or daughter to use various machines, tools, and materials. They will construct products as they perform activities designed to teach and reinforce concepts that are basic to understanding the technical world in which we live.

Safety will be stressed throughout the course, and the proper use of tools and machines will be demonstrated. Before a student will be allowed to operate any power equipment or work in the technology lab, he or she must achieve a perfect score on all safety tests, demonstrate the correct operation of all tools and machines, express and show a proper attitude about safety, and submit a completed and signed "Emergency Information Form."

The "Emergency Information Form" is enclosed with this letter and must be completed by each parent/guardian before students begin their work in the technology lab. Please return it promptly for our emergency files. Be sure to check the information carefully and sign the form.

If you have any questions or comments about our program, please feel free to contact me at your convenience during school hours. I encourage YOUR involvement.

Sincerely,

Technology Teacher

_____
*Motto of the Technology Student Association

(continued next page)

Emergency Information Form

Please PRINT or TYPE all emergency information.

Student's Name _____ Age _____

Address _____ Home Phone _____

City _____ Zip Code _____

Family Doctor _____ Phone _____

Address _____

City _____ Zip Code _____

In case of serious injury, please notify _____

During school hours, they can be reached at: Home _____ Work _____

Name of Business _____

Address _____ City _____

Phone _____ Extension _____

Confidential Information

Note: If necessary, write additional comments on the back of this sheet.

Does the student have any physical or mental impairments that may be of concern to me as a technology educator or that might affect the safe operation of the program at school? _____

If so, please specify: _____

_____

Is this student on medication of any type that may limit activities or affect vision, hearing, balance, or other senses? _____

If so, please specify: _____

_____

Is the student allergic to any medications? _____

If so, please specify: _____

_____

As the parent/guardian of the above mentioned child, I have read the attached information sheet and I promise the preceding information is true and correct. I will inform the technology teacher of any changes which may occur this year regarding my child and the safe operation of this program.

Signature _____ Date _____

Thank you for your understanding and candidness concerning the above information. This should help our program be as safe as possible for all concerned.

General Safety Study Sheet

Safety must always be uppermost in your mind when you work in the lab. Study the following list of safety rules carefully. You will be tested. More importantly, though, knowing and following these rules will help keep you and your classmates safe as you work in the lab. Remember, the safe way is *always* the best way.

Attitude

- Horseplay will not be tolerated. This is evidence of a poor safety attitude.
- Each person's safety is everyone's responsibility.
- Mistakes cause accidents.
- The number one cause of accidents is a poor attitude.
- Read and follow all posted safety rules.
- Keep your mind on your work.

Clothing and Protective Equipment

- Always wear proper eye protection when working in the lab.
- Never wear jewelry or loose clothes in the lab.
- Wear an apron while using tools or machines.
- Tie long hair back or wear it under a cap to avoid getting it caught in machinery.
- Wear hard shoes or boots with rubber soles.
- Use ear protection near loud equipment.

Working with Tools and Machines

Before use:
- Don't use any equipment until the teacher has shown you how to use it and has given you permission.

- You must get the teacher's permission before you use any equipment, even if you have used it before.
- Don't use any equipment unless the teacher is in the lab.
- Obtain the right tool for the job. The most important reason for using the right tool for the job is safety.
- Tell the teacher immediately if a machine doesn't sound right, or if you can see that something is wrong.
- Make certain that the teacher has checked the setup before turning on power machinery.
- Make certain that you and others stay out of the danger zones marked by red or red/white striped tape around machines.
- When you approach a machine, be sure it is off and that it is not coasting.
- Before working on stock (wood or other workpieces), check it for cracks, loose knots, and nails.
- Be sure blades, belts, and bits are installed properly before using tools.
- You must be able to measure before you can use most power equipment.
- Plan your work; measure twice and cut once.

During use:
- Use the right tool for the job.
- Take your time when working with tools.
- Use only tools that are sharp and in good condition. Handle sharp tools carefully.
- Carry sharp or pointed tools with the point down.
- Handle materials with sharp edges and pointed objects carefully.

(continued next page)

TECHNOLOGY INTERACTIONS Teacher's Resource Guide

- Use special care with heated materials and devices that get hot.
- When operating any machine, give it all of your attention.
- Use machine guards at all times to prevent injury.
- Always secure your work with a clamp or vise.
- The *shortest* piece of lumber that can safely be run through most equipment is 12 inches long.
- Never talk to a person while he/she is operating a machine.
- Support long stock when cutting.
- Wait until the blade stops before removing any scraps.
- Use care and common sense when working with electrical devices and equipment.
- Be sure the power is off and the blade has stopped before making adjustments.
- Disconnect the cord from the power source before changing bits, belts, or blades.
- Allow machines to reach full speed before starting to cut.
- Avoid standing in danger zones.
- Never distract the machine operator.
- Never place your hand or fingers in line with any moving parts.
- Never set a hand-held power tool down while it is running or coasting.
- If you have to leave a machine, turn it off and wait until it stops.
- Do not overreach; keep your balance.
- Use only properly insulated or grounded tools.
- Stand to one side when using power tools.

- Use compressed air with caution and only with the teacher's permission.

After use:
- When you finish using a machine, turn it off, wait until it stops, and clean the machine and the area around it.
- Pull the plug, not the cord, when you unplug a machine.
- Damaging the cord of electrical hand-held tools may cause an electric shock.
- Return all tools and unused supplies to their proper places when you have finished working.

Fire Prevention
- Before using any equipment, know where the fire extinguishers are located and how to use them.
- Keep oily rags in a closed metal container to prevent spontaneous combustion.

Lab Maintenance
- Keep the floor and aisles clean at all times.
- If a liquid is spilled, clean it up immediately as instructed by the teacher.
- Always use a brush to clean dry materials from a table or piece of equipment.
- Store all materials properly.

Health
- Lift with your legs, not your back.
- Get help to lift or move long or heavy objects or materials.
- Work in a well-ventilated area.
- If you do not feel well, tell the teacher and do not work in the lab.
- If there is an accident—even a minor one—report it immediately to the teacher.

Name _____ Class _____ Date _____

General Safety Test

Directions: Correctly complete the following safety rules by filling in the blank with the proper word or words.

Attitude

1. _____ will not be tolerated. This is evidence of a poor safety attitude.
2. Each person's _____ is everyone's responsibility. Work safely and make sure others work safely.
3. Mistakes cause _____.
4. The number one cause of accidents is a poor _____.
5. Read and follow all posted _____.
6. Keep your _____ on your work.
7. The safe way is _____ the best way.

Clothing and Protective Equipment

8. Always wear proper _____ when working in the lab.
9. Never wear _____ or loose clothes in the lab.
10. Wear a(n) _____ while using tools or machines.
11. _____ should be tied back or worn under a cap to avoid getting it caught in the machinery.
12. You should wear _____ or boots with rubber soles.
13. When equipment is _____, use ear protection.

Working with Tools, Machines, and Other Equipment

Before use:

14. Don't use any equipment until the _____ has shown you how to use it and has given you permission.
15. You must get the teacher's permission before you use any _____, even if you have used it before.
16. Don't use any equipment unless the _____ is in the lab.
17. Obtain the right tool for the job. The most important reason for using the right tool for the job is _____.
18. Tell the teacher _____ if a machine doesn't sound right, or if you can see that something is wrong.
19. Make certain the teacher has checked the _____ before turning on power machinery.
20. Make certain that you and others stay out of the _____ marked by red or red/white striped tape around machines.

(continued next page)

TECHNOLOGY INTERACTIONS Teacher's Resource Guide
Copyright © Glencoe/McGraw-Hill

21. When you _____ a machine, be sure it is off and that it is not coasting.
22. Before working on _____ (wood or other workpieces), check it for cracks, loose knots, and nails.
23. Be sure blades, belts, and bits are _____ properly before using.
24. You must be able to _____ before you can use most power equipment.
25. _____ your work; measure twice and cut once.

During use:
26. Use the _____ tool for the job.
27. Take your _____ when working with tools.
28. Use only tools that are _____ and in good condition. Handle sharp tools carefully.
29. Carry sharp or pointed tools with the point _____.
30. Handle materials with _____ and pointed objects carefully.
31. Use special care with heated materials and devices that get _____.
32. When operating any machine, give it all of your _____.
33. Use machine _____ at all times to prevent injury.
34. Always secure your work with a(n) _____ or vise.
35. The shortest piece of lumber that can safely be run through most equipment is _____ long.
36. Never talk to a person while he/she is _____ a machine.
37. _____ stock must be supported when cutting.
38. Wait until the blade _____ before removing any scraps.
39. Use care and _____ when working with electrical devices and equipment.
40. Be sure the power is off and the blade has stopped before making any _____.
41. The cord must be disconnected from the power source before _____ bits, belts, or blades.
42. Machines should be allowed to reach full speed _____ starting to cut.
43. Avoid standing in _____.
44. Never _____ the machine operator.
45. Never place your hand or fingers in line with any _____ parts.
46. Never set a hand-held power tool down while it is _____ or coasting.
47. If you have to _____ a machine, turn it off and wait until it stops.
48. Do not _____; keep your balance.
49. Use only properly insulated or _____ tools.
50. _____ to one side when using power tools.

(continued next page)

51. Use _____ with caution and only with the teacher's permission.

After use:

52. Pull the _____, not the cord, when you unplug a machine.

53. Damaging the cord of electrical hand-held tools may cause a(n) _____.

54. Return all _____ and unused supplies to their proper places when you are finished working.

Fire Prevention

55. Before using any equipment, you should know where the _____ are located and how to use them.

56. Oily rags must be kept in a closed metal container to prevent _____.

Lab Maintenance

57. Keep the floor and aisles _____ at all times.

58. If a liquid is spilled, clean it up _____ as instructed by the teacher.

59. Always use a(n) _____ to clean dry materials from a table or piece of equipment.

60. When you finish using a machine, turn it off, wait until it stops, and _____ the machine and the area around it.

61. Store all _____ properly.

Health

62. Lift with your _____, not your back.

63. Get help to _____ or move long or heavy objects or materials.

64. Work in a(n) _____ area.

65. If you do not feel well, tell the_____ and do not work in the lab.

66. If there is a(n) _____—even a minor one—report it immediately to the teacher.

Name _____ Class _____ Date _____

Safety Pledge

Technology Department

I pledge to obey all safety rules and regulations concerning the tools, materials, and equipment in the Technology lab. I will not place myself or others in danger by my actions or behavior (horseplay, etc.). I will not operate any tool or equipment, or use any material without prior instruction and approval from the teacher. I must also score 100% on required safety tests before operating any of the equipment/tools. Failure to comply with this pledge is grounds for temporary or permanent removal from the lab and/or other appropriate disciplinary or legal action.

Date:_____ Signature: _____

Safety Signs

The following signs may be reproduced for classroom use. You may wish to post them on or near machinery and equipment or in prominent areas around the lab.

Safety Instruction Required Before Operating Any Equipment

Be Careful

The SAFE WAY Is Always the BEST WAY

Eye Protection Required

In This Lab

Think!

Accidents Are Avoidable

RETURN TOOLS

To Their Proper Places

Do NOT Distract Machine Operators

Lesson Plans

This part contains one lesson plan for each chapter in the text. Each lesson plan includes the following: a RESOURCES section, which lists products that can be used to supplement the chapter material; a FOCUS section, which includes an overview, a list of the chapter's objectives, and a "Tying to Previous Knowledge" part; a TEACH section, which includes teaching suggestions and answers to "Linking to Mathematics" and "Check Your Facts" from the student text; an ASSESS section, which includes "Meeting Chapter Objectives," "Evaluate," "Reteach," and "Enrich" parts; and a CLOSE section, which includes tips for the "Apply What You've Learned" activity from the student text.

Date		M	Tu	W	Th	F

Lesson Plan for Chapter 1

How Technology Works

Resources

Technology Today and Tomorrow
  © 1999 – Chapter 1
Introduction to Technology
  © 1999 – Chapter 1
Experience Technology: Communication, Production, Transportation, Biotechnology © 1997 – Chapter 1

FOCUS

Overview

Chapter 1 focuses on the development of technology and the forces that shaped that development. The chapter examines the four families of technology, the needs they satisfy, and the impact they have had on society.

Objectives

- Describe the relationship between human needs and technology.
- Identify the seven resources upon which all technologies depend.
- Describe and give examples of manufacturing, construction, transportation, communication, and bio-related technologies.
- Explain the similarities shared by all technological systems.
- Describe and give examples of technological impacts.

Tying to Previous Knowledge

Ask students if they remember the first video game they ever played. Have them describe the complexity of the game, the graphic images, and the mobility of the game characters. Ask students to compare that game to the newest, most recent game they have played. How has the technology changed? Do they find the newer games more satisfying? Does technology always get more complicated as it tries to satisfy new needs?

TEACH

Teaching Suggestions

1. **Demonstration.** Show a variety of early technological devices. This might include tools, cameras, radios, cooking utensils, tape recorders, or toys. Compare these to their modern counterparts. Lead a discussion on why the design changes took place.
2. **Discussion.** Have students look around the room, look out the window, or envision their own home. Ask students to place the products of technology they see into the categories of the four families of technology. Ask them to identify the needs and wants satisfied by each of these products.
3. **Problem Solving.** Ask students to imagine that they were stranded on an uninhabited tropical island for a long period of time. How would they use the resources available to satisfy their most basic needs? What products would they need to create?
4. **Design and Build Activity:** "A Lifting Device." Make connections to early structures. How were the stones of the pyramids and the great cathedrals lifted into place? How are the beams and columns of modern construction maneuvered into place? Stress that technology is the application of science. Review simple machines and mechanical advantage. Expand the activity to include gears, pulleys, and other simple machine combinations.

(continued next page)

5. **Careers.** Have students complete **Career Activity 1.** (Reproducible Career Activity masters and an Answer Key are in Part IV of this teacher's resource guide.) Students will need to look in the *Occupational Outlook Handbook,* either in print form or on the Internet. On the Internet, the URL is http://stats.bls.gov/ocohome.htm. Once at the site, students can do a keyword search for the desired career.

Answer to "Linking to Mathematics"

- 374,400 air bags

Answers to "Check Your Facts"

1. The following needs and wants are basic to all people: food, water, shelter, communication, transportation, recreation, protection, and health care.
2. When people change resources into products to satisfy a need, they are creating technology.
3. The seven resources upon which all technologies depend are: people, information, time, materials, energy, tools/machines, and money.
4. Manufacturing systems produce products in factories; construction systems create structures, usually on the site where they will be used. Communication systems help people gather, store, and share information in a variety of ways. Transportation systems move people, products, and materials from one place to another. Bio-related technologies use microorganisms to process materials and help create better connections between technologies and the people who use them.
5. Technological systems allow us to input either resources or commands. Manufacturing systems take in resources and convert them into products. All systems have a process section. The process section transforms the resources or carries out the commands. All systems have outputs. The output is what the system actually accomplishes.

ASSESS

Meeting Chapter Objectives

Have students complete **Chapter Review 1.** (Reproducible Chapter Review masters and an Answer Key are in Part IV of this teacher's resource guide.)

Evaluate

Have students complete **Chapter Test 1.** (Reproducible Chapter Test masters and an Answer Key are in Part IV of this teacher's resource guide.)

Reteach

To many people, the word *technology* automatically brings thoughts of computers and robots. It is important for students to understand that technology has existed since the beginning of time. Technology is not a product; it is a process. This process has had a tremendous effect on people since humans first began walking the planet.

Enrich

The impacts of technology are not always positive. Have students investigate negative impacts of technological systems. Pick a technological system such as an automobile and model an improvement to the system that helps correct its negative outputs.

CLOSE

Have students complete the **Apply What You've Learned Activity:** "Design and Build a Profile Map of an Ocean Floor." This activity will take approximately three to five days to complete. Make the connections to early techniques used in map making. Show pictures of early navigation equipment and early maps. Explain how sonar actually works. Give other examples of how sonar technology is used. How were ocean floor maps made before sonar technology?

Date		M	Tu	W	Th	F

Lesson Plan for Chapter 2

Design and Problem Solving

Resources

Technology Today and Tomorrow
© 1999 – Chapter 2
Introduction to Technology
© 1999 – Chapter 2
Glencoe Physical Science © 1997 – Each
chapter has at least one design activity.
*Experience Technology: Communication,
Production, Transportation,
Biotechnology* © 1997 – Chapter 10

FOCUS

Overview

Chapter 2 covers the design process and how it can be used to solve real problems. The six-step process will guide students in the development of solutions to the design-and-build activities found in each chapter of this text.

Objectives

• Define design.
• Explain how problem solving is part of designing.
• Explain the steps of the design process.
• Describe a variety of modeling techniques.
• Use the design process to solve real problems.

Tying to Previous Knowledge

Give students a 3″ × 5″ card and ask them to write down one school or community problem that needs to be solved. Select several problems for discussion. Ask: Are these real problems? What are some possible solutions?

TEACH

Teaching Suggestions

1. **Demonstration.** Show students how to use the brainstorming process to generate ideas. Ask them to identify other situations in which brainstorming would be useful.
2. **Discussion.** Explain how invention and innovations are different. Ask students to describe some of their favorite inventions and innovations.
3. **Problem Solving.** Create a brief hands-on activity such as constructing the tallest possible tower using limited materials. Emphasize the design process and working as a team.
4. **Design and Build Activity:** "A Floor Plan." This activity will take three days and will introduce drawing to scale and enable students to apply concepts learned in mathematics. Have several books of house plans, home magazines, and furniture advertisements available as resource materials.
5. **Design and Build Activity:** "A Time-Keeping Device." Research is the key to this activity. Have books available that describe early time-keeping devices. Sundial construction allows you to introduce some mathematics beyond measuring. Expand the activity to include devices used to keep track of the months. Explore how digital watches work. Display the works of a mechanical watch.
6. **Careers.** Have students complete **Career Activity 2.** (Reproducible Career Activity masters and an Answer Key are in Part IV of this teacher's resource guide.) Students will need to look in the *Occupational Outlook Handbook,* either in print form or on the Internet. On the Internet, the URL is http://stats.bls.gov/ocohome.htm. Once at the site, students can do a keyword search for the desired career.

(continued next page)

Lesson Plan for Chapter 2 (continued)

Answers to "Check Your Facts"

1. Design is a plan for making something.
2. Problem solving can be used to help arrive at the best design for a needed product or service.
3. Invention is the designing of new products. Innovation occurs when an existing technology is improved.
4. The steps in the problem solving process are: identify the need, gather information, develop alternative solutions, choose the best solution, implement the solution, and evaluate the solution.
5. The design brief should clearly state the problem and include details about the materials to be used, how much can be spent, and when the solution is needed.
6. Good sources of information include people, libraries, museums, and the Internet.
7. Two-dimensional modeling techniques include sketching, drawing, and rendering. Sketches provide ideas that can be used for more detailed drawings. Renderings are color drawings that resemble finished products.
8. Appearance models resemble finished products, but they do not work. Prototypes are models that look and work like the finished product.
9. Ergonomics is the matching of design to human needs.

ASSESS

Meeting Chapter Objectives

Have students complete **Chapter Review 2.** (Reproducible Chapter Review masters and an Answer Key are in Part IV of this teacher's resource guide.)

Evaluate

Have students complete **Chapter Test 2.** (Reproducible Chapter Test masters and an Answer Key are in Part IV of this teacher's resource guide.)

Reteach

Students may have difficulty with the concept of ergonomics. Use a desk and adjustable chair to demonstrate comfortable and uncomfortable seating positions.

Enrich

Students who finish early or who need a more challenging activity can construct a 3D solution for one of the situations described in the chapter.

CLOSE

Have students complete the **Apply What You've Learned Activity:** "Design and Build a Spreadsheet." This activity will take two days. Show students several sample spreadsheets. Demonstrate the use of the tutorials and manuals that accompany spreadsheet programs.

Date		M	Tu	W	Th	F

Lesson Plan for Chapter 3

Computer-Aided Drafting (CAD)

Resources

Technology Today and Tomorrow
© 1999 – Chapter 9
Introduction to Technology
© 1999 – Chapter 6
*Experience Technology: Communication,
Production, Transportation, Biotechnology*
© 1997 – Chapter 13

FOCUS

Overview

Chapter 3 discusses computer-aided drafting (CAD), including its advantages and how it is used in industry.

Objectives

- Explain the advantages of CAD.
- Identify the components of a CAD system.
- Discuss how CAD is used in industry.
- Describe the basic CAD system commands.

Tying to Previous Knowledge

Ask students why drawings are important. What is the difference between technical drawing and fine art? Name careers that require technical drawing and artistic skills. (architecture, advertising, industrial design)

TEACH

Teaching Suggestions

1. **Demonstration.** Show how to start up the CAD system and use basic commands. Complete a simple drawing using traditional drafting techniques and CAD. Based on the demonstration, ask students to describe some of the advantages of CAD.
2. **Discussion.** Show students a simple product. Ask them to describe the drawings that would be needed to produce it accurately.
3. **Reinforcement.** Systems are an important part of technology. Name the input, process, and output components of a typical CAD system. (input: keyboard, mouse, digitizing tablet; process: CAD software and CPU; output: monitor and plotter)
4. **Background.** Although CAD is replacing traditional drafting in most industries, the ability to express ideas using sketches remains important. Quick sketches are a good way to capture ideas and explore alternative solutions prior to using CAD.
5. **Design and Build Activity:** "A Site Plan." This activity will take two days and demonstrates an important advantage of CAD. Ask students to identify the advantages and disadvantages of designing a building for a particular site.
6. **Design and Build Activity:** "A Tic-Tac-Toe Board." This activity will take two days. During this activity, students will become familiar with basic CAD commands.
7. **Careers.** Have students complete **Career Activity 3.** (Reproducible Career Activity masters and an Answer Key are in Part IV of this teacher's resource guide.) Students will need to look in the *Occupational Outlook Handbook,* either in print form or on the Internet. On the Internet, the URL is http://stats.bls.gov/ocohome.htm. Once at the site, students can do a keyword search for the desired career.

Answers to "Check Your Facts"

1. CAD is faster, neater, and more accurate than traditional drafting.

(continued next page)

2. CAD systems require hardware and software. Hardware includes a fast, powerful computer; input devices such as the keyboard, mouse, and digitizing tablet; and output devices such as a monitor and printer or plotter. Software: many different CAD programs are available.
3. Two-dimensional drawings show width and length, width and height, or length and height. Three-dimensional drawings also show depth.
4. CAD is used to design buildings, to design manufactured products, and as part of the CAD/CAM process.
5. Three categories of commands are drawing, editing, and utility.

ASSESS

Meeting Chapter Objectives

Have students complete **Chapter Review 3.** (Reproducible Chapter Review masters and an Answer Key are in Part IV of this teacher's resource guide.)

Evaluate

Have students complete **Chapter Test 3.** (Reproducible Chapter Test masters and an Answer Key are in Part IV of this teacher's resource guide.)

Reteach

Some students may have difficulty using the CAD system. Encourage students to work in pairs. Remind them to take advantage of the pull-down Help menu. Provide individual help as needed. Create a display of CAD drawings that includes the work of beginners and advanced students.

Enrich

Students who finish early or need a more challenging activity can select or be assigned an interesting problem from a CAD textbook. Display quality work.

CLOSE

Have students complete the **Apply What You've Learned Activity:** "Orthographic Projection." This activity will take approximately three days. Have students experiment using isometric graph paper for entering X, Y, and Z coordinates before using the CAD system.

Date		M	Tu	W	Th	F

Lesson Plan for Chapter 4

Desktop Publishing

Resources

Technology Today and Tomorrow
  © 1999 – Chapter 7
*Experience Technology: Communication,
  Production, Transportation, Biotechnology*
  © 1997 – Chapter 12
Introduction to Technology
  © 1999 – Chapter 7
The New Way Things Work © 1998

FOCUS

Overview

Computers have dramatically changed and simplified printing. This chapter covers the basics of desktop publishing and some of the things that need to be considered when designing a document for publication.

Objectives

• Define desktop publishing.
• Identify the software and hardware needed for desktop publishing.
• Identify the three main categories of typefaces.
• Describe some of the important factors that must be considered when designing a document.

Tying to Previous Knowledge

Ask students to describe how they use computers at home and school. Many students now use computers for assignments such as essays and reports. What are some of the advantages of this? (faster, neater, corrections and revisions are easy to make) Are there any disadvantages? Discuss any suggestions students offer.

TEACH

Teaching Suggestions

1. **Demonstration.** Show how to use desktop publishing software. Import previously word-processed text, and select and place clip art. Print a hard copy and make changes based on suggestions by students. If available, show students how to use related equipment such as a scanner and digital camera.

2. **Discussion.** Ask students to identify the kinds of articles their classmates would like to see included in a school publication (sports, interviews, reviews, surveys). Use these ideas to explain the importance of considering the audience when planning and preparing a publication.

3. **Background.** Use several recent newspaper articles of interest to students to show how they include the five "w's": who, what, when, where, and why. Have students use these as they prepare a brief article describing a recent technology class activity.

4. **Design and Build Activity:** "An Advertisement." This activity will take two days. Have each student bring in a magazine ad for a product that appeals to young people. Discuss how art and text can be combined to communicate the desired message. Ask students to incorporate the ideas discussed in their advertisements.

5. **Design and Build Activity:** "A Document." This activity will take one day and will give students the opportunity to integrate writing and technology skills. Students should explain what they liked or disliked about the music, film, or book they are reviewing and state why they do or do not recommend it.

6. **Careers.** Have students complete **Career Activity 4.** (Reproducible Career Activity

(continued next page)

masters and an Answer Key are in Part IV of this teacher's resource guide.) Students will need to look in the *Occupational Outlook Handbook,* either in print form or on the Internet. On the Internet, the URL is http://stats.bls.gov/ocohome.htm. Once at the site, students can do a keyword search for the desired career.

Answer to "Linking to Mathematics"

• 58.5 square inches.

Answers to "Check Your Facts"

1. Desktop publishing is the use of a computer and special software to produce documents such as newsletters, catalogs, and textbooks.
2. Desktop publishing requires a computer with a lot of memory and a monitor, scanner, and printer.
3. A typeface is a set of letters, numbers, and symbols that look the same.
4. Type is measured in points.
5. The main categories of typefaces are serif, sans serif, and decorative.
6. Drawings and photographs are graphics that can be used in desktop publishing. They can be obtained by using clip art or by scanning existing photographs or artwork.
7. Three kinds of scanners are hand-held, flat-bed, and sheet-fed. Scanners change images into an electronic form that computers can use.
8. Important factors to be considered when designing a document include: Who will read it? What interests the readers? How long should it be? How will it be reproduced?

ASSESS

Meeting Chapter Objectives

Have students complete **Chapter Review 4.** (Reproducible Chapter Review masters and an Answer Key are in Part IV of this teacher's resource guide.)

Evaluate

Have students complete **Chapter Test 4.** (Reproducible Chapter Test masters and an Answer Key are in Part IV of this teacher's resource guide.)

Reteach

Use examples of student-prepared articles and advertisements to highlight the features of well-designed documents.

Enrich

Students who finish early or need a more challenging activity can prepare a set of questions that will be used during the interview of a student or staff member who has a unique hobby or interest. Later, students can conduct the interview and publish their articles.

CLOSE

Have students complete the **Apply What You've Learned Activity:** "Design and Build a Newsletter." This is an ideal team activity and will take approximately five days. Organize students so that they contribute to both the writing and production aspects of the publication. After careful editing, duplicate the newsletter. Ask other teachers to use it as part of their class activities.

Date		M	Tu	W	Th	F

Lesson Plan for Chapter 5

Computer Animation

Resources

Technology Today and Tomorrow
© 1999 – Chapter 4

FOCUS

Overview

Chapter 5 covers the animation process. Three types of animation and the role of computers in the animation process are described.

Objectives

- Discuss the uses of animation.
- Identify the information included on a storyboard.
- Compare the three types of animation.
- List the six steps in three-dimensional computer animation.

Tying to Previous Knowledge

Show brief segments from two animated films: one produced with cel animation (e.g., *Snow White*), and the other produced with computer animation (e.g., *Toy Story*). Ask students to describe the similarities and differences.

TEACH

Teaching Suggestions

1. **Demonstration.** Show students how to use a computer animation program. If the program includes a tutorial, cover its use. Later, have students present their animations.
2. **Discussion.** Many of the techniques used in early animation are important in modern computer animation. Explain that skills such as design and timing are important for all types of animation. Use this as an opportunity to discuss how new technologies frequently evolve from early, simple processes and products.
3. **Reinforcement.** Compare computer-aided drafting and computer animation. Several major software developers produce CAD and animation programs. Computers have dramatically changed both drafting and animation in recent years. Both fields give people an opportunity to combine technical and fine art skills.
4. **Design and Build Activity:** "A Flip-Book." This activity will take about two days and will help students learn the basics of animation. Have students share their flip-books with other class members.
5. **Design and Build Activity:** "A Thaumatrope." This activity will take one day and involves students in making a toy of historical importance. Relate to Linking to Science in the textbook. Discuss the importance of persistence of vision in toys, television, and computer animation.
6. **Careers.** Have students complete **Career Activity 5.** (Reproducible Career Activity masters and an Answer Key are in Part IV of this teacher's resource guide.) Students will need to look in the *Occupational Outlook Handbook,* either in print form or on the Internet. On the Internet, the URL is http://stats.bls.gov/ocohome.htm. Once at the site, students can do a keyword search for the desired career.

Answers to "Linking to Mathematics"

- $560,000
- $420,000
- $3,360,000
- yes; $2,380,000

(continued next page)

Answers to "Check Your Facts"

1. Animation is used to create cartoons, films, video games, and commercials.
2. Persistence of vision is the blending of individual images into one that seems to move. Before the brain has finished processing one image, it receives another.
3. Storyboards show action and spoken words and guide the development of a film.
4. In hand-drawn animation, a series of drawings are photographed. Each drawing makes up one frame of the film. In model animation, puppets are photographed on a set one frame at a time. Computer animation can be used to produce an entire cartoon or film from start to finish, or it can be used to speed up the traditional cel animation process.
5. Claymation is a kind of model animation that uses three-dimensional figures made of clay. The models are photographed on a set one frame at a time. After each photograph, the models are adjusted and another photograph is made.
6. The steps in three-dimensional computer animation are storyboards, modeling, animation, shading, lighting, and rendering.
7. A cel is a drawing of one frame on a clear plastic sheet. Completed cels are photographed frame by frame over background scenes.
8. Primitives are basic geometric shapes produced by a 3D computer modeling program.
9. A key frame is a frame that shows a beginning or ending point in an action sequence.
10. Shading makes animation more realistic by adding color and texture.

ASSESS

Meeting Chapter Objectives

Have students complete **Chapter Review 5.** (Reproducible Chapter Review masters and an Answer Key are in Part IV of this teacher's resource guide.)

Evaluate

Have students complete **Chapter Test 5.** (Reproducible Chapter Test masters and an Answer Key are in Part IV of this teacher's resource guide.)

Reteach

Some students may have difficulty using computer animation software. Encourage students to work in pairs and complete the entire tutorial. Provide individual help as needed.

Enrich

Students who finish early or need a more challenging activity can use the Internet to learn more about computer animation and view animations created by hobbyists and professionals.

CLOSE

Have students complete the **Apply What You've Learned Activity:** "Design and Build a Zoetrope." This activity will take one to two days. Team members should contribute by drawing pictures and/or constructing the zoetrope wheel. After initial testing, have students make changes to improve the illusion of motion.

Name _____ Class Period _____ Time _____

Date	M	Tu	W	Th	F

Lesson Plan for Chapter 6

Internet

Resources

Technology Today and Tomorrow
© 1999 – Chapter 5

FOCUS

Overview

The Internet is bringing about many changes. This chapter covers how the Internet works, some of its important uses, and how it affects our lives.

Objectives

- Identify what is needed to access the Internet.
- Explain Internet safety and etiquette.
- Explain the purpose of a hyperlink.
- Explain the parts of an e-mail address.

Tying to Previous Knowledge

Ask students to compare the Internet to other communication systems. What are some advantages of the Internet? (speed and quality of information available) Are there disadvantages? (Not everyone can afford access, and some of the information on the Internet is not accurate.)

TEACH

Teaching Suggestions

1. **Demonstration.** Show students how to get on the Internet and use it to gather information on a technology-related topic. Use several search engines and explain techniques for narrowing down research when too many sites are identified.
2. **Reinforcement.** Compare the Internet to other systems. What does it have in common with other computer-based technologies such as CAD and CNC? (changing rapidly and input, process, output)

3. **Discussion.** Many people are concerned about material on the Internet that is offensive or inappropriate. Some schools and families have installed software to block access to certain sites. Discuss whether this is a good idea.
4. **Background.** Use recent newspaper and magazine advertisements to show students that many companies and organizations are using Web sites to describe the products and services they offer. Access several sites so that students can compare and evaluate what they offer.
5. **Design and Build Activity:** "An Internet Report." This activity will take three days and will enable students to learn more about the Internet and how it can be used for research. Use the activity to integrate language arts and technology concepts. Help students revise the reports so that they are clearly written and technically accurate.
6. **Design and Build Activity:** "A Timeline." This activity will take approximately three days. Assign students to cover overlapping periods of time so that they can compare what they learned to the information gathered by others.
7. **Careers.** Have students complete **Career Activity 6.** (Reproducible Career Activity masters and an Answer Key are in Part IV of this teacher's resource guide.) Students will need to look in the *Occupational Outlook Handbook,* either in print form or on the Internet. On the Internet, the URL is http://stats.bls.gov/ocohome.htm. Once at the site, students can do a keyword search for the desired career.

Answer to "Linking to Mathematics"

- It will take Company A 44,642.9 seconds (744 minutes) to transmit its daily data. At 8¢ per minute, their daily telephone charge is $59.52.

(continued next page)

Answers to "Check Your Facts"

1. A computer network is a communication system created by connecting many computers.
2. To get on the Internet you need a computer, a modem, a telephone line, communication software, and an Internet service provider. The computer is the device most commonly used to access the Internet. A modem changes the signals from the computer into signals that can be transmitted over telephone lines. Communication software connects the computer to the Internet through a company called an *Internet service provider.*
3. Most Web sites contain hyperlinks. When you click on them, they take you to other Web pages.
4. An Internet e-mail address such as "jsmith@tech.org" has three parts. Before the "@" is the user's name (jsmith). After the "@" is the domain (tech), which is the name of the Internet provider. The third part is the zone (.org).
5. A mailing list is a discussion group for people interested in a particular topic. E-mail sent to a mailing list is received by everyone on the list.

ASSESS

Meeting Chapter Objectives

Have students complete **Chapter Review 6.** (Reproducible Chapter Review masters and an Answer Key are in Part IV of this teacher's resource guide.)

Evaluate

Have students complete **Chapter Test 6.** (Reproducible Chapter Test masters and an Answer Key are in Part IV of this teacher's resource guide.)

Reteach

Students may have difficulty in selecting key words that will help them locate the information they want. Demonstrate the use of several different search engines to point out specific features and the advantages and disadvantages of each.

Enrich

Students who finish early or who need a more challenging activity can use the Internet to learn more about a related topic, such as career clusters or specific job opportunities of interest. You may wish to require students to obtain your approval before beginning their research.

CLOSE

Have students complete the **Apply What You've Learned Activity:** "Design and Build a Home Page." This activity will take approximately three days. Encourage students to think about how having a Web site can help both individuals and businesses.

Name _____ Class Period _____ Time _____

Date		M	Tu	W	Th	F

Lesson Plan for Chapter 7

Audio, Video, and Multimedia

Resources

Technology Today and Tomorrow
© 1999 – Chapter 6
The New Way Things Work
© 1998 – Information about
photography, sound and video recording

FOCUS

Overview

We live in the information age. This chapter covers audio, video, and multimedia communication and describes some of the great changes that electronic communication is creating today and in the future.

Objectives

- Explain the terms *audio, video,* and *multimedia.*
- Identify three ways television signals can be received in homes.
- Define sound.
- Explain what multimedia is and give examples of how it is used.

Tying to Previous Knowledge

Use a survey to ask students about television viewing habits. How much television do they watch each day? Provide students with the raw data and have them calculate the average daily viewing time for their class. Also, have students discuss what they would do if they were not able to watch television for an extended period of time.

TEACH

Teaching Suggestions

1. **Demonstration.** Use an educational CD-ROM such as an encyclopedia to show students how these programs are interactive. Cover use of hypertext and hotspots to visit other parts of the program. Compare to Internet links.
2. **Discussion.** Ask students to contribute to a discussion on the positive and negative aspects of television. How do they feel about the violence portrayed in many popular programs? Does this contribute to violence in the community?
3. **Problem Solving.** Tell students that their class has been selected to produce a five-minute video broadcast for the school. Use the brainstorming process to generate ideas about what should be included. If time permits, prepare a prototype broadcast.
4. **Design and Build Activity: "A Storyboard."** This activity will take approximately three days and will help students plan for an actual television news broadcast. To help students get started, display several storyboards used for previous broadcasts.
5. **Design and Build Activity: "A Megaphone."** This activity will take one day. Provide students with a variety of cone and fastening materials. Encourage students to use the problem solving process to develop several alternative designs as they work to create a good solution to this problem.
6. **Careers.** Have students complete **Career Activity 7.** (Reproducible Career Activity masters and an Answer Key are in Part IV of this teacher's resource guide.) Students will need to look in the *Occupational Outlook Handbook,* either in print form or on the Internet. On the Internet, the URL is http://stats.bls.gov/ocohome.htm. Once at

(continued next page)

the site, students can do a keyword search for the desired career.

Answer to "Linking to Mathematics"

- 0.1198 of a second (approximately ⅛ second)

Answers to "Check Your Facts"

1. Audio is something we hear. Video is something we see. Multimedia combines several forms of communication.
2. Video switching is done in a television control room by a technician. A "switcher" is used to select the camera specified by the director. It is also used to "cut" to commercials.
3. Television signals can be received in the home by antenna, cable, or satellite system.
4. Sound is a form of energy produced by vibrations that act on the ear so that we can hear.
5. The main parts of a radio are an antenna, a tuner, amplifiers, and one or more speakers.
6. Multimedia is the combination of several kinds of communication, such as text, pictures, sound, video, and animation. Examples of multimedia include television, the Internet, computer animations, video games, and video-on-demand.

ASSESS

Meeting Chapter Objectives

Have students complete **Chapter Review 7.** (Reproducible Chapter Review masters and an Answer Key are in Part IV of this teacher's resource guide.)

Evaluate

Have students complete **Chapter Test 7.** (Reproducible Chapter Test masters and an Answer Key are in Part IV of this teacher's resource guide.)

Reteach

Some students may have difficulty distinguishing between amplitude modulation (AM) and frequency modulation (FM). Draw several different waves and label the wavelength, frequency, and amplitude. Ask students to describe AM and FM broadcasting using sketches and a brief verbal or written explanation.

Enrich

Students who finish early or who need a more challenging activity can prepare an audio or video program and present it to the entire class.

CLOSE

Have students complete the **Apply What You've Learned Activity:** "Design and Build a Tin Can Telephone." This activity will take one day and will help students understand transmission of sound through solid materials.

Date		M	Tu	W	Th	F

Lesson Plan for Chapter 8

Manufacturing

Resources

Technology Today and Tomorrow
© 1999 – Section 3 (six chapters)
Introduction to Technology
© 1999 – Chapters 10 & 11
Experience Technology: Communication, Production, Transportation, Biotechnology
© 1997 – Section 5 (six chapters)

FOCUS

Overview

Manufacturing is an important part of most modern economics. Chapter 8 covers some of the important materials, processes, and impacts of manufacturing today and in the future.

Objectives

- Describe the difference between natural and synthetic materials.
- Name primary and secondary processes.
- List the basic steps in the manufacturing system.
- Describe the three types of production systems used in manufacturing.
- Describe how computers are used in computer-integrated manufacturing.

Tying to Previous Knowledge

Ask students to identify five items they use on a daily basis. Discuss where and how the items were produced. Were they made in a factory? Where they grown on a farm? How many can be made at home? Which items were available 50 or 100 years ago? Where were they made then?

TEACH

Teaching Suggestions

1. **Demonstration.** Show students how to combine cement, sand, and gravel to produce concrete, a composite and important building material. Use the concrete for a school project or to make bars that can be tested for strength.
2. **Discussion.** Use examples to explain how automation can create new jobs and make others obsolete. Ask students to describe how this impacts people. Discuss what workers can do to reduce the possibility of losing their jobs in the changing workplace.
3. **Problem Solving.** Assign students to research one of the forming processes. Have them apply what they have learned by making a simple device that demonstrates the process.
4. **Design and Build Activity:** "A Mass-Produced Item." The time required to complete this activity depends on the item selected for production. Have teams of two students produce prototypes. Then guide the class in selecting one for mass production. Demonstrate proper use of any equipment and supplies required for the activity.
5. **Design and Build Activity:** "An Assembly System." This activity can be completed in one class period. Purchase a quantity of inexpensive, retractable ballpoint pens. Emphasize that this is an opportunity to engage in a process that is becoming increasingly important in industry.
6. **Careers.** Have students complete **Career Activity 8.** (Reproducible Career Activity

(continued next page)

masters and an Answer Key are in Part IV of this teacher's resource guide.) Students will need to look in the *Occupational Outlook Handbook,* either in print form or on the Internet. On the Internet, the URL is http://stats.bls.gov/ocohome.htm. Once at the site, students can do a keyword search for the desired career.

Answer to "Linking to Mathematics"

- 243 posts

Answers to "Check Your Facts"

1. Natural materials are found in nature. Synthetic materials are made by people. Wood and clay are natural materials. Plastics and ceramics are synthetic materials.
2. A composite is a material made by combining two or more materials. The materials that form a composite are not changed.
3. Primary processes are processes that change raw materials into industrial materials.
4. Secondary processes are processes that turn industrial materials into finished products.
5. Rolling, casting, and forging are examples of forming processes.
6. The three types of conditioning are thermal, chemical, and mechanical.
7. The manufacturing system includes design and engineering, purchasing, production, distribution, and sales.
8. In custom production, products are made to order. During job-lot production, a specific quantity of a product is made. In continuous production, products are mass-produced, usually on an assembly line.
9. In computer-integrated manufacturing, computers monitor and control every aspect of production.
10. The gross domestic product is the total value of goods and services produced each year.

ASSESS

Meeting Chapter Objectives

Have students complete **Chapter Review 8.** (Reproducible Chapter Review masters and an Answer Key are in Part IV of this teacher's resource guide.)

Evaluate

Have students complete **Chapter Test 8.** (Reproducible Chapter Test masters and an Answer Key are in Part IV of this teacher's resource guide.)

Reteach

Many students have difficulty with linear measurement. Review the standard and metric systems and explain their use in quality control. Give students an opportunity to work with instruments such as rules, micrometers, and calipers.

Enrich

Students who finish early or who need a more challenging activity can use the Internet to learn more about manufacturing. Many major manufacturers have Web sites that describe interesting aspects of production.

CLOSE

Have students complete the **Apply What You've Learned Activity:** "Design and Build Product Packaging." This activity will take approximately two days. Individually wrapped mints or other candies are recommended. Display a variety of disassembled packages to give students ideas. Have students explain why their design will help increase sales.

Date		M	Tu	W	Th	F

Lesson Plan for Chapter 9

Structures

Resources

Science Interactions: Course 4
  © 1999 – Unit 5 (five chapters)
*Experience Technology: Communication,
  Production, Transportation, Biotechnology*
  © 1997 – Section 6 (four chapters)
Introduction to Technology
  © 1999 – Chapter 12
Technology Today and Tomorrow
  © 1999 – Section 4 (five chapters)
Structures: The Way Things Are Built
  © 1993
Architecture © 1997
Treehouses © 1994
Why Buildings Fall Down © 1992

FOCUS

Overview

Chapter 9 explains that building a structure is a system that includes inputs, processes, outputs, and feedback. Some of the important things that must be considered during the planning and construction of a structure are described.

Objectives

- Identify the four parts of a system.
- Describe the loads and forces that act on structures.
- Be able to explain the difference between a static load and a dynamic load.
- Identify the main parts in the system used to build a house.

Tying to Previous Knowledge

Ask students to describe some of the structures they see and use every day. What do they have in common? How do they differ? Use a familiar local structure to review the system components (input, process, output, feedback).

TEACH

Teaching Suggestions

1. **Demonstration.** Show students the forces of tension, compression, shear, and torsion using materials such as a sponge, rope, paper, and rubber bands. Ask students to describe other examples of the forces and describe how they apply to structures.
2. **Discussion.** Ask students to think about a future dream house. What will it include? Why? What new technologies will be incorporated? What will be necessary so that the dream becomes reality?
3. **Background.** Create a bulletin board of drawings and photographs made by students to show the wide range of structures found in the community (residential, commercial, industrial, and civil). Use the display to discuss the needs they satisfy.
4. **Reinforcement.** Show examples that demonstrate that information in the form of graphs and tables can clearly communicate the data gathered during testing.
5. **Design and Build Activity: "A Testing Station."** This activity will take one day. Using inexpensive materials, students will learn that shape can play an important role in determining the strength of structural members. Use class discussion to compare the data collected by the various student teams.

(continued next page)

6. **Careers.** Have students complete **Career Activity 9.** (Reproducible Career Activity masters and an Answer Key are in Part IV of this teacher's resource guide.) Students will need to look in the *Occupational Outlook Handbook,* either in print form or on the Internet. On the Internet, the URL is http://stats.bls.gov/ocohome.htm. Once at the site, students can do a keyword search for the desired career.

Answer to "Linking to Mathematics"

- 22 feet

Answers to "Check Your Facts"

1. The four parts of a system are inputs, process, outputs, and feedback.
2. A spider web, a bird nest, and a wasp nest are examples of natural structures.
3. Static loads, such as the weight of the materials used to build a structure, change slowly or not at all. Dynamic loads move or change.
4. Forces on a structure can be external or internal. Static and dynamic loads are external forces. Internal forces that act within a structure include tension, compression, shear, and torsion.
5. The internal force present in a twisted beam is torsion.
6. The major force that the foundation of a home must withstand is compression.
7. Beams are horizontal structural members. Columns are vertical structural supports.
8. Before designing a home, an architect needs information such as who will live in the house, the kind of lot, how many bedrooms are needed, when the house needs to be completed, and how much money can be spent to build the home.
9. The foundation, or substructure, is the part of the structure that is in contact with the ground. The superstructure is the part of the structure that is above (and is supported by) the foundation.
10. Like all systems, building systems include inputs, processes, outputs, and feedback.

ASSESS
Meeting Chapter Objectives

Have students complete **Chapter Review 9.** (Reproducible Chapter Review masters and an Answer Key are in Part IV of this teacher's resource guide.)

Evaluate

Have students complete **Chapter Test 9.** (Reproducible Chapter Test masters and an Answer Key are in Part IV of this teacher's resource guide.)

Reteach

Some students may have difficulty with activities that involve linear measurement. A class pre-test can be used to identify students who require additional assistance.

Enrich

Encourage students who finish early or who need a more challenging activity to work as a team to construct an architectural model of a vacation home using foam-core board as the basic building material.

CLOSE

Have students complete the **Apply What You've Learned Activity:** "Design and Build a Small Structure." This activity will take two days to complete. Review concepts related to static and dynamic loads. Compute several examples of strength-to-weight ratio. If possible, videotape the testing to aid in analyzing students' design and construction techniques.

Date			M	Tu	W	Th	F

Lesson Plan for Chapter 10

Flight

Resources

Science Interactions: Course 4
© 1999 – Unit 7 (three chapters) Excellent coverage of all kinds of flight.
Technology Today and Tomorrow
© 1999 – Chapter 22
Introduction to Technology
© 1999 – Chapter 14
Boeing 747-400 © 1998
Boeing 777 © 1998
Mighty Machines – Airplane
© 1995
The New Way Things Work
© 1998
Visual Dictionary of Flight
© 1992

FOCUS

Overview

Chapter 10 takes a broad look at aerospace technology. Flight will be addressed from the scientific view of forces acting upon things that fly, as well as the technological aspects of design, control, and power.

Objectives

• Describe the forces that oppose motion.
• Identify and discuss the forces that allow an airplane to fly.
• Identify and discuss the processes used to control flight in an airplane.

Tying to Previous Knowledge

Ask students if they have ever flown in an airplane or sat at an airport and watched the huge aircraft lift gently off the ground. Follow up by asking what forces are working on the aircraft trying to prevent it from rising off the runway. What forces must the aircraft produce to overcome these forces? Where and how does the aircraft produce these forces?

TEACH

Teaching Suggestions

1. **Demonstration.** Show how the movement of air across a tissue reduces air pressure, causing the tissue to rise or lift. This is done by suspending the tissue from the two top corners and blowing down the front of the tissue.
2. **Discussion.** Ask students what portion of the aircraft creates lift by speeding up the movement of air across its surface.
3. **Background.** Hand out photographs, diagrams, and models of various airplane designs. Have students study the shapes of the wing and the surface area of the wing in relationship to the size of the aircraft.
4. **Problem Solving.** Ask the students what effect changing the profile shape of the wing would have on its ability to create a lifting force.
5. **Design and Build Activity: "An Airfoil."** This activity should take three to four days. Be sure the airfoils have enough surface area difference (top and bottom of the airfoil) to create lift. Be sure the air strikes the leading edge of the airfoil.

(continued next page)

6. **Design and Build Activity: "A Rocket."** This activity should take one to two days, depending on the number of tests students perform. Be sure the film canisters have the internal cap locks, not the external type. It can take 15 to 30 seconds before enough gas builds up to have lift-off.

7. **Careers.** Have students complete **Career Activity 10.** (Reproducible Career Activity masters and an Answer Key are in Part IV of this teacher's resource guide.) Students will need to look in the *Occupational Outlook Handbook,* either in print form or on the Internet. On the Internet, the URL is http://stats.bls.gov/ocohome.htm. Once at the site, students can do a keyword search for the desired career.

Answers to "Check Your Facts"

1. The force of surface friction keeps Sarah's sneakers gripped to the rough surface of the skateboard.
2. Friction and gravity are two forces that oppose motion.
3. Lift and thrust help airplanes overcome the force of gravity.
4. The surfaces of the aircraft's ailerons, rudder, and elevators control the flight of the plane. These surfaces create drag and lift as a means of turning, climbing, and descending the aircraft. The rudder turns the nose of the aircraft left and right. The elevators move the nose up and down. The ailerons help the aircraft to bank.
5. Drag and lift are the forces acting on the airplane's wing flaps.

ASSESS
Meeting Chapter Objectives

Have students complete **Chapter Review 10.** (Reproducible Chapter Review masters and an Answer Key are in Part IV of this teacher's resource guide.)

Evaluate

Have students complete **Chapter Test 10.** (Reproducible Chapter Test masters and an Answer Key are in Part IV of this teacher's resource guide.)

Reteach

Students have a difficult time understanding the concept of air pressure and the Bernoulli effect. Have students perform the "tissue lift" test described earlier.

Enrich

To challenge students with more ability, ask them to design and build a helicopter rotor system and test it in the same manner used to test the propeller. The blades should be adjustable to increase and decrease lift.

CLOSE

Have students complete the **Apply What You've Learned Activity:** "Design and Build a Propeller." This activity should take two to three days to complete. Students must understand that "bigger is not always better." Large propellers spin at lower speeds, reducing the amount of air moved. The shape and angle of attack will determine the efficiency of these propeller models.

Date				M	Tu	W	Th	F

Lesson Plan for Chapter 11

Land and Water Transportation

Resources

Introduction to Technology
  © 1999 – Chapter 14
*Experience Technology: Communication,
Production, Transportation, Biotechnology*
  © 1997 – Chapter 31
Technology Today and Tomorrow
  © 1999 – Section 5 (four chapters that
  cover all types of transportation)

FOCUS

Overview

Chapter 11 examines land and water transportation modes. Included in the chapter is a discussion of the historical developments in transportation systems and power systems used in transportation.

Objectives

• Describe various modes of land and marine transportation.
• Discuss power sources used in transportation.
• Describe the operation of a four-stroke cycle gasoline engine.

Tying to Previous Knowledge

Have students divide into teams. Have each team create a list of as many modes of transportation as they can think of. Place the lists on the board. Take a survey to see how many students have actually used the modes listed on the board.

TEACH

Teaching Suggestions

1. **Demonstration.** Demonstrate the forces of repulsion used in some magnetic levitation vehicles. Demonstrate the force of compressed gas in a cylinder by gently shaking a liter bottle of soda. Have students feel the pressure exerted on the sides of the container by the expanding gases. Demonstrate the force of buoyancy by creating a hull from a sheet of paper that will support fifty pennies in water.

2. **Discussion.** "In today's society, the ability to move people and products is as crucial to life as food itself." Begin a discussion with your class focused on this statement. Do students agree or disagree with the statement? Can they support their opinions with facts?

3. **Reinforcement.** The goal of transportation systems is to move people, products, and materials quickly and efficiently from one point to another. Trace the development of transportation systems. For land transportation, compare travel from New York to California during the Gold Rush period to today's modes of transportation. Compare speed, time, efficiency, and comfort. For water transportation systems, compare crossing the Atlantic from New York to England during the same time periods.

4. **Background.** The study of transportation systems lends itself nicely to the study of systems in general. With students, produce a large systems diagram that illustrates the range of systems from large global systems to smaller subsystems within a vehicle or vessel. For example, start with the Interstate Highway System in the United States. Use a branching diagram and include bridges, tunnels, highways, parkways, and maintenance systems. Pick a vehicle such as the family automobile and break it down into its subsystems, such as ignition, lubrication, exhaust, and safety. Break those subsystems down into even smaller subsystems, such as the battery or air bag.

5. **Design and Build Activity:** "A Model Maglev System." This activity can take many weeks, depending on how you design the challenge.

(continued next page)

The simplest approach is to have students design and model a body and chassis that levitates on a short, 12″ guideway. To expand the activity, ask students to model the interior of the vehicle or produce a wind-powered vehicle that travels down a long test guideway. Try placing the guideway at an incline and having students conduct experiments comparing the effect of the mass and the angle of incline on the speed of the vehicles.

6. **Design and Build Activity:** "A Cam Operating System." Cam actions are used in many transportation subsystems. Rods, lifters, pistons, and rail car wheels depend on cam actions. This activity demonstrates the relationship between the cam shape and the direction of motion. Rather than cutting cam lobes, students can drill an off-center hole in a disc to achieve the same effect. Animating puppets is a fun topic to incorporate cam action. Juice and milk containers make quick housings.

7. **Careers.** Have students complete **Career Activity 11.** (Reproducible Career Activity masters and an Answer Key are in Part IV of this teacher's resource guide.) Students will need to look in the *Occupational Outlook Handbook,* either in print form or on the Internet. On the Internet, the URL is http://stats.bls.gov/ocohome.htm. Once at the site, students can do a keyword search for the desired career.

Answer to "Linking to Mathematics"

• 339.5 miles

Answers to "Check Your Facts"

1. Automobiles, trains, planes, and ships are all examples of transportation modes.
2. Diesel locomotives require less maintenance and refueling and burn cleaner.
3. Affordability, speed, and comfort have led to increased rail travel in the United States.
4. Most modern locomotives use diesel-electric power. Some systems pull electric power from ground or overhead rails to power electric motors that turn the wheels.
5. Mass production techniques made the automobile an affordable mode of transportation.
6. *Intake stroke*—Fuel enters the cylinder. *Compression stroke*—Fuel is compressed and ignited.

Power stroke—The expanding gases caused by ignition of the compressed fuel forces the piston down the cylinder. *Exhaust stroke*—The piston moves back up the cylinder to exhaust the unburned gasoline and waste gases.
7. On-site transportation includes conveyor belts, pipe lines, elevators, and escalators.
8. It allows the vessel to carry larger cargo and provides more room for storage.
9. The purpose of the hull (speed or cargo), the type of water in which the vessel will travel, and the comfort of the ride provided by the vessel must be considered.
10. Most modern marine vessels are propelled by wind, diesel engines, or water jets.

ASSESS
Meeting Chapter Objectives

Have students complete **Chapter Review 11.** (Reproducible Chapter Review masters and an Answer Key are in Part IV of this teacher's resource guide.)

Evaluate

Have students complete **Chapter Test 11.** (Reproducible Chapter Test masters and an Answer Key are in Part IV of this teacher's resource guide.)

Reteach

Focus again on alternatives to present transportation systems, including electric vehicles, new fuels, and new mass transit systems.

Enrich

Have students model the Euro Chunnel, which connects France and England under the English Channel.

CLOSE

Have students complete the **Apply What You've Learned Activity:** "Design and Build a Catamaran." This activity may take one to two weeks to complete. Keeping the hulls as far apart as possible provides the stability needed to overcome the force of the wind in the sails. Students should experiment with different sail shapes and materials.

Date		M	Tu	W	Th	F

Lesson Plan for Chapter 12

Fluid Power

Resources

Experience Technology: Communication, Production, Transportation, Biotechnology © 1997 – The activity that begins Section 5 describes how to use fluid power to control a robot.
Introduction to Technology © 1999 – Chapter 17

FOCUS

Overview

Chapter 12 covers hydraulic and pneumatic fluid power systems. The basic components of fluid power systems and their use in manufacturing, construction, agriculture, and health care are described.

Objectives

- Define fluid power.
- Explain the difference between hydraulic and pneumatic systems.
- Identify the basic components of fluid power systems.
- Give examples of how fluid power is used.
- Discuss the future of fluid power.

Tying to Previous Knowledge

Remind students that air and water are necessary for life. Ask them to describe examples of using air and water to do work (examples: sailboats, using wind and water power to generate electricity). Why is air consider to be a liquid? (It flows.)

TEACH

Teaching Suggestions

1. **Demonstration.** Show how water falling from a faucet can operate a simple turbine (waterwheel). Use the rotating shaft of the turbine to operate a small DC motor. Use a galvanometer to show that electricity is being generated.
2. **Discussion.** Ask students to discuss the pros and cons of using air bags in motor vehicles. What tradeoffs are involved? Remind students that air bags are designed to be used with seat belts.
3. **Reinforcement.** Fluid power systems can be used to create mechanical advantage. Review how pulleys and gears can also be used to produce mechanical advantage.
4. **Problem Solving.** Connect two plastic syringes using a short length of tubing. Operate using air and water. Ask students to describe what they observe and feel.
5. **Design and Build Activity:** "A Water Squirter." This activity will take three days. Instruct students in the proper use of tools and machines for the activity. Set up a suitable area for students to test their water squirters. Ask students to think of other uses for similar systems, such as irrigation and fire fighting.
6. **Design and Build Activity:** "An Air Cushion Vehicle." This activity will take one to two days. STudents should record their results in a table. Have students demonstrate their best air cushion vehicle.
7. **Careers.** Have students complete **Career Activity 12.** (Reproducible Career Activity

(continued next page)

masters and an Answer Key are in Part IV of this teacher's resource guide.) Students will need to look in the *Occupational Outlook Handbook,* either in print form or on the Internet. On the Internet, the URL is http://stats.bls.gov/ocohome.htm. Once at the site, students can do a keyword search for the desired career.

Answer to "Linking to Mathematics"

- 12.56 square inches

Answers to "Check Your Facts"

1. Fluid power is the use of pressurized liquids or gases to perform tasks such as moving heavy objects.
2. Hydraulic systems use oil or another liquid. Pneumatic systems use air or another gas.
3. Fluid power system components include fluid, compressor or pump, reservoir or receiver, control valves, actuators, flow regulators, and transmission lines.
4. Actuators change pressure into mechanical motion.
5. Drawings used to represent fluid power systems are schematic circuit diagrams. They are read from bottom to top.
6. Manufacturing—hydraulic lifts for moving materials; transportation—automobile steering and air bags; construction—nailers and heavy equipment; agriculture—planting and harvesting equipment.

ASSESS

Meeting Chapter Objectives

Have students complete **Chapter Review 12.** (Reproducible Chapter Review masters and an Answer Key are in Part IV of this teacher's resource guide.)

Evaluate

Have students complete **Chapter Test 12.** (Reproducible Chapter Test masters and an Answer Key are in Part IV of this teacher's resource guide.)

Reteach

Some students will have difficulty with the concept of mechanical advantage. Review the example in Fig. 12-7 in the textbook, and have students calculate pressure for several similar problems.

Enrich

Students who finish early or who need a more challenging activity can use syringes, tubing, wheels, and assorted building materials to construct a working model of an aircraft landing gear.

CLOSE

Have students complete the **Apply What You've Learned Activity:** "Design and Build a Gameboard." this activity will take approximately five days. Demonstrate proper use of tools and machines that students will need for the activity. Students should let classmates test their games to obtain feedback that will suggest improvements.

Date		M	Tu	W	Th	F

Lesson Plan for Chapter 13

Health Technologies

Resources

Technology Today and Tomorrow
© 1999 – Check the index for many topics on health concerns and health care.

Experience Technology: Communication, Production, Transportation, Biotechnology
© 1997 – Chapter 20

Introduction to Technology
© 1999 – Chapter 15

The New Way Things Work
© 1998

FOCUS

Overview

Chapter 13 focuses on the health fields associated with bio-related technologies. This includes the development of physical enhancements such as prostheses, as well as equipment for medical diagnosis and treatment. The chapter concludes with an overview of ergonomics.

Objectives

• Describe five of the technological activities associated with health technologies.
• Define biomechanical engineering.
• Discuss the impacts of technology on diagnosis in medicine.
• Identify future trends in bio-related technology.
• Identify the items a human factors engineer must consider in making a design.

Tying to Previous Knowledge

Ask students what they think the current life ex-

pectancy is for Americans. Follow up this question with a guesstimate of the life expectancy of Americans 200 years ago. Lead a discussion focused on why and how Americans have been able to increase their life expectancy. Make a list of medical interventions that have made the quality and health of our lives better today than it was 200 years ago.

TEACH

Teaching Suggestions

1. **Demonstration.** Demonstrate a variety of home healthcare devices. These might include blood sugar testing kits, home blood pressure testing equipment, and breathing aids such as a nebulizer and spirometer. Some of these devices may be available from the school nurse. Ask students to bring in devices they use to help them stay healthy. Local orthopedic surgeons might be willing to donate replacement joints. Prosthesis manufacturers often lend prosthetic devices to schools for examination.

2. **Discussion.** Lead a discussion focused on medical procedures that students might have experienced or know about. This may include procedures such as magnetic resonance imaging, orthoscopic surgery, X-rays, and sonograms.

3. **Problem Solving.** Ask students what they would do if they were confined to a chair for an extended period of time due to an injury. How would they modify the chair to meet their new needs more effectively?

4. **Design and Build Activity:** "A Human Joint Replacement." Many mechanical joints used in machinery mimic human joints. Hinge joints, ball-and-socket joints, and gliding joints are found in many devices. Have the

(continued next page)

students research how these joints are made and where they are used in the body. Students can construct these joints out of a variety of materials. Emphasize that the joints they are creating are models and do not have to be made out of exotic materials.

5. **Design and Build Activity:** "An Assisted-Living Product." Many pharmacy and health aid stores sell assisted-living devices. Have students visit the store and sketch some ideas. Invite a physically challenged person into your class and have a discussion focused on everyday activities that present difficulties. Students' fingers, hands, knees, and other joints can be taped together to simulate a physical challenge.

6. **Careers.** Have students complete **Career Activity 13.** (Reproducible Career Activity masters and an Answer Key are in Part IV of this teacher's resource guide.) Students will need to look in the *Occupational Outlook Handbook,* either in print form or on the Internet. On the Internet, the URL is http://stats.bls.gov/ocohome.htm. Once at the site, students can do a keyword search for the desired career.

Answer to "Linking to Mathematics"
• 8

Answers to "Check Your Facts"

1. Health technology activities include development of diagnosis equipment, treatment equipment, and replacement body parts, as well as the manufacture of new drugs and vaccines, and genetic engineering processes.
2. Biomechanical engineering is the use of engineering processes and design principles to solve medical problems.
3. A prosthesis is a body replacement part that is made by people.
4. X-rays, MRI, and sonograms are examples of medical diagnostic technologies.
5. Health technologies have extended the length and quality of life. Unfortunately, the cost of such services are high and out of reach for some people.
6. Genetic engineering is the process of changing genetic material in order to modify genes, which are the building blocks of all living things.

7. Ergonomics is the study of the design of equipment and processes to improve the match between people and the machines they use every day.
8. Human factors engineers must consider the strengths and limitations of the human body.
9. Wheelchair accessibility requires wider doorways and hallways to accommodate the width of the chair. Grab bars and rails are essential. Apartment designs must also include closets and counter heights that are easily accessible from the height of the chair.

ASSESS
Meeting Chapter Objectives

Have students complete **Chapter Review 13.** (Reproducible Chapter Review masters and an Answer Key are in Part IV of this teacher's resource guide.)

Evaluate

Have students complete **Chapter Test 13.** (Reproducible Chapter Test masters and an Answer Key are in Part IV of this teacher's resource guide.)

Reteach

Students do not associate the engineering aspects of technology with medicine. Help students understand that engineers, industrial designers, and technicians, as well as doctors and nurses, are responsible for medical improvements.

Enrich

The manufacture of soft tissue replacement materials such as skin, tendons, and arteries is a cutting edge technology. Have students research and report on new discoveries in these areas. The use of robotics in surgery is also an interesting field.

CLOSE

Have students complete the **Apply What You've Learned Activity:** "Design and Build a New Computer Keyboard." This is an ergonomic engineering activity. The placement of the more frequently used keys under the stronger fingers underlines the principles of human factors design. Challenge students to develop ways of measuring finger strength and mobility.

Date		M	Tu	W	Th	F

Lesson Plan for Chapter 14

Environmental Technologies

Resources

Experience Technology: Communication, Production, Transportation, Biotechnology © 1997 – Check the index for several entries about the environment.
Technology Today and Tomorrow © 1999 – Check the index for many topics on the environment.
Science Interactions: Course 4 © 1999 – Many topics are listed in the index under "Ecosystems."

FOCUS

Overview

Chapter 14 examines the families of bio-related technologies associated with the environment and environmental problems. These technologies include controlled environment agriculture, genetic engineering, bioprocessing, and other aspects of food production, plant propagation, and environmental cleanup.

Objectives

- Identify the five activities involved in traditional soil farming.
- Identify the advantages of controlled environment agriculture (CEA). Identify two products created by bioprocessing.
- Give one example of a bioprocessing technique used to process materials.
- Discuss the impacts of bio-related technologies.

Tying to Previous Knowledge

Ask students the following questions: Have they ever eaten a seedless grape? How do farmers remove the seeds? What ingredient gives yogurt its distinctive taste? How can we grow food on the moon where there is no soil? The answers to all these questions lie in the study of bio-related technologies. Bio-related technologies are technologies that use and later living organisms to produce products and improve production.

Distribute seed packages and have students read the characteristics guaranteed by the manufacturer. How can the manufacturer guarantee these results?

Bring in several different types of apples. Ask students how a farmer can combine the best traits of each apple into one super apple.

TEACH

Teaching Suggestions

1. **Demonstration.** Show students a string bean plant growing in nutrient solutions without soil. Show students how to sprout mung beans in a damp paper towel. Graft a different variety of apples to the root stock of an apple tree.

2. **Discussion.** Ask students what biological function determines height, eye color, and hair color. Discuss recent news articles that focus on genetic engineering as a way of preventing disease.

3. **Design and Build Activity:** "A Hydroponic Growing System." Beans and marigold

(continued next page)

plants sprout quickly and grow fairly fast. The wick system works well for most plants. Fabric from discarded T-shirts, preferably a blend of 50% cotton and 50% polyester does a great job. Water alone has enough nutrients for the plant until it reaches approximately 3″ to 4″ in height. Commercially available plant food is then required. This activity will take approximately five to seven days.

4. **Design and Build Activity:** "A Plant Watering Device." A gravity feed system is a very practical solution. A fine wire drill can be used to open a drip spout in a discarded beverage container cap. Students will have to experiment with the size of the hole and the size of an air escape hole in the bottle.

5. **Careers.** Have students complete **Career Activity 14.** (Reproducible Career Activity masters and an Answer Key are in Part IV of this teacher's resource guide.) Students will need to look in the *Occupational Outlook Handbook,* either in print form or on the Internet. On the Internet, the URL is http://stats.bls.gov/ocohome.htm. Once at the site, students can do a keyword search for the desired career.

Answers to "Linking to Mathematics"

- 441 apples
- 4,410 seeds
- 17,503,290

Answers to "Check Your Facts"

1. Photosynthesis is the process plants use to change sunlight into energy. Chlorophyll in the plant traps light and helps the plant change water and carbon dioxide into sugar and oxygen.
2. The five main activities in traditional soil farming are clearing the soil, tilling the soil, planting the seeds, cultivating the crops, and harvesting the crops.
3. Farmers select the members of the herd that produce the most milk and mate them with the strongest, leanest bulls. The result is off-spring that produce large quantities of milk.
4. Farmers use seeds that are genetically engineered to be resistant to certain diseases.
5. Branches of different varieties of apples are grafted onto the root stock of an apple tree.

6. CEA allows the farmer to create the specific environment a plant needs to thrive.
7. Hydroponics grows food and plants in a soil-less environment. Traditional farming uses soil as the growing medium.
8. Yogurt and bread are created through bio-processing techniques.
9. In bread, yeast cells digest sugar and starch and create carbon dioxide, which makes the bread rise.
10. Bio-related technologies have helped make farms more productive. Bio-related technologies have also developed techniques to clean up polluted water ways.

ASSESS

Meeting Chapter Objectives

Have students complete **Chapter Review 14.** (Reproducible Chapter Review masters and an Answer Key are in Part IV of this teacher's resource guide.)

Evaluate

Have students complete **Chapter Test 14.** (Reproducible Chapter Test masters and an Answer Key are in Part IV of this teacher's resource guide.)

Reteach

The concept of microorganisms (things they can't see) processing materials may be difficult for students to understand. Try to make the connection to bacteria and viruses (germs) that cause the common cold. Students cannot see those organisms either, but they certainly feel their effects.

Enrich

Using an inexpensive kit, students can make their own yogurt in the classrooms.

CLOSE

Have students complete the **Apply What You've Learned Activity:** "Casein Glue Manufacturing System." This activity will take approximately three to four days. Students can also use the glue they produce to make a product. Try casting the glue in a mold. It will set up like a plastic.

Date		M	Tu	W	Th	F

Lesson Plan for Chapter 15

Electricity and Electronics

Resources

Introduction to Technology
  © 1999 – Chapter 9
Science Interactions: Course 4
  © 1999 – Chapter 19
Glencoe Physical Science
  © 1997 – Chapter 21 has excellent
  coverage of electricity.
The New Way Things Work © 1998

FOCUS

Overview

Chapter 15 introduces the basic principles behind electricity, electricity production, and the relationship between voltage, current, and resistance. The chapter also provides an introduction to electronics and electronic components.

Objectives

- Describe the relationships among voltage, current, and resistance.
- Explain the basic organization of a series circuit and a parallel circuit.
- Describe the operation and uses of diodes and transistors.
- Explain the operation of an electronic device in terms of input, process, and output.

Tying to Previous Knowledge

Ask students what factors contribute to how long a battery will last in a flashlight before it runs out of electrical energy. Ask students what happens to the brightness of the bulb as the energy decreases. Does temperature affect the life of the battery? Talk about other familiar devices that use electrical energy. Do batteries in a Walkman style radio last longer when the radio is being used or when the cassette player is being used? What factors influence the energy force traveling through electrical conductors?

TEACH

Teaching Suggestions

1. **Demonstration.** Show how electrical energy can be generated by breaking a magnetic field with a coil of wire. Cut open a "D" cell and a 9-volt battery so students can see the chemistry.
2. **Discussion.** Discuss the difference between static electricity and flowing electricity. Discuss typical energy transformations that take place in everyday electrical devices (flashlight, toaster, etc.). Discuss the voltaic cell used on calculators. Why aren't batteries needed?
3. **Background.** Understanding the atomic model is essential to student understanding of the production and flow of electricity. Make connections between the forces of attraction between electrons within the atom and magnetic forces. This helps students understand how the electrons flow through a conductor.
4. **Problem Solving.** Give students a bulb, wire, switch, and "D" cell. Ask them to assemble a flashlight circuit. Give students two "C" cells, a 1.5-V piezo buzzer, a photoresistor, and some wire. As students to assemble a circuit that will turn the buzzer off when the sun goes down.
5. **Design and Build Activity:** "An LED Warning System." The LEDs have polarity. Students must be careful how they wire them into the circuit. Have students list devices or places

(continued next page)

they have seen flashing LEDs as an indicator or warning light. If students place nonflashing LEDs in series with the flashing LED, they will flash also. A microchip built into the lens of the flashing LED controls the rate at which it flashes.

6. **Careers.** Have students complete **Career Activity 15.** (Reproducible Career Activity masters and an Answer Key are in Part IV of this teacher's resource guide.) Students will need to look in the *Occupational Outlook Handbook,* either in print form or on the Internet. On the Internet, the URL is http://stats.bls.gov/ocohome.htm. Once at the site, students can do a keyword search for the desired career.

Answer to "Linking to Mathematics"

• 150 ohms

Answers to "Check Your Facts"

1.

2. EMF (electromotive force) causes electrons to flow.
3. Electrons in the outer shells of the atom are held to the atom by a weaker force than those in the inner shells.
4. Chemical energy in a battery can apply EMF. Breaking magnetic fields on a generator also applies EMF.
5. Ohm's law states that current is equal to the voltage divided by the resistance of a circuit $(I = E/R)$.
6. Transistors miniaturize and reduce the energy consumed by electronic circuits.
7. A series circuit is one in which there is only one path for electricity to flow through. A parallel circuit provides multiple paths for electricity to flow through.
8. The most common use of diodes is to change alternating current into direct current. The diode only allows electrons to flow through the junction in one direction.
9. All electronic systems take input and change

it into electronic signals. The systems then process or do something with the signal that produces a desired output.

10. Transistors have many uses in an electronic circuit. Their primary job is to act as an electronic switch. A transistor can control large amounts of electricity by regulating the flow of tiny amounts of electricity at its junctions.

ASSESS

Meeting Chapter Objectives

Have students complete **Chapter Review 15.** (Reproducible Chapter Review masters and an Answer Key are in Part IV of this teacher's resource guide.)

Evaluate

Have students complete **Chapter Test 15.** (Reproducible Chapter Test masters and an Answer Key are in Part IV of this teacher's resource guide.)

Reteach

The principle behind semiconductor operation is complex. If students have trouble understanding how semiconductors operate, help them concentrate on common uses. At middle-school level, the application of the component is more important than the physics of the device.

Enrich

Give students a variety of electronic components and have them design their own circuits. For example, challenge them to build a circuit that turns a fan on when the lights go out, or one that turns on a buzzer when the temperature rises above a certain point.

CLOSE

Have students complete the **Apply What You've Learned Activity:** "Design and Build a Continuity Tester." This activity will take two days. Encourage students to suggest other materials to test. After obtaining your approval, have them test these materials also.

Date		M	Tu	W	Th	F

Lesson Plan for Chapter 16

Computer Control Systems

Resources

Technology Today and Tomorrow
© 1999 – Chapter 13
Experience Technology: Communication, Production, Transportation, Biotechnology
© 1997 – Chapter 21

FOCUS

Overview

Chapter 16 focuses on the use of computers in manufacturing. It describes computer applications used in product design, as well as machine and production line control

Objectives

- Describe how computers are used to design products.
- Explain the process of computer numerical control.
- Identify manufacturing systems that depend upon computers.

Tying to Previous Knowledge

Ask students how computers have changed their everyday lives. Where do they come in contact with computers each day? Remind students that computers control many things and may be hidden from view. Have students list their experiences. Then ask them how they think computers have changed the way products are manufactured in a factory.

TEACH

Teaching Suggestions

1. **Demonstration.** Demonstrate a CAD or paint program that can be used in the design phase of manufacturing. If available, demonstrate the operation of a robotic arm or CNC machine. Show a video of these machines in operation on an actual assembly line.

2. **Discussion.** Ask students to suggest possible advantages and disadvantages of computerization of manufacturing. What impacts might it have on product costs? on employment?

3. **Reinforcement.** Automobile manufacturing reflects all aspects of computerization in manufacturing. Show a video that illustrates CAD, CIM, and CNC in the automobile industry. Ask students how computerization helped American manufacturing become more competitive in the world market.

4. **Problem Solving.** Ask students how computers could help classroom instruction and the teaching/learning process. if each desk were equipped with a computer system, how should it be used by the student and the teacher?

5. **Design and Build Activity:** "A Product Concept." Simple paint programs can be learned quickly and are easy to use. Have students brainstorm design ideas. Evaluate keychains that students have in their pockets or book bags. Demonstrate the use of multiview drawings. Have students explore pictorial drawings on the computer.

6. **Design and Build Activity:** "A Flowchart." Have students develop flow charts for common daily activities such as making a peanut-butter and jelly sandwich or brushing their teeth. Allow teams of students to show their charts and take input as to how they can streamline the process. This is a paper-and-pencil activity, but it can be expanded to produce simple products that can be mass-produced in one class period.

7. **Careers.** Have students complete **Career Activity 16.** (Reproducible Career Activity masters and an Answer Key are in Part IV of this teacher's resource guide.) Students will need to look in the *Occupational Outlook Handbook,* either in print form or on the Internet. On the Internet, the URL is

(continued next page)

http://stats.bls.gov/ocohome.htm. Once at the site, students can do a keyword search for the desired career.

Answer to "Linking to Mathematics"

• 1,252 inches

Answers to "Check Your Facts"

1. Computers are used in manufacturing to help in the design, production, and organization of the manufacturing process.
2. Engineers often use computer-aided design software (CAD) to draw plans for products.
3. Animation and simulation software can help test products during the design phase without actually making prototypes and models.
4. CNC machines use computers that have been programmed to guide the machine through its operations. This may include cutting, grinding, and assembly operations.
5. The CNC programmer feeds locations or points to the machine through a computer. The coordinates, as they are called, are locations along imaginary X, Y, and Z axes. The X axis runs parallel to the floor from left to right. The Y axis also runs parallel to the floor, but up and down through the material. The Z axis runs at right angles to the X and Y axes and perpendicular to the floor. Any area on the material can be identified by an X,Y,Z location.

ASSESS

Meeting Chapter Objectives

Have students complete **Chapter Review 16.** (Reproducible Chapter Review masters and an Answer Key are in Part IV of this teacher's resource guide.)

Evaluate

Have students complete **Chapter Test 16.** (Reproducible Chapter Test masters and an Answer Key are in Part IV of this teacher's resource guide.)

Reteach

Students may have difficulty imagining the X, Y, and Z axes. Set up a box made from clear acrylic plastic. Place an acetate grid on the front, one side, and the top of the box to represent the X, Y, and Z grids. Hang a marble from a thread inside the box. Have students mark the location of the marble on the X, Y, and Z acetate grids.

Enrich

Have students write a program for a CNC machine or robotic arm.

CLOSE

Have students complete the **Apply What You've Learned Activity:** "Design and Build Computer Numerical Control Coordinates." Plotting coordinate pairs is commonly taught in math class as part of a graphing unit. See if a math teacher will team-teach the activity with you. Math teachers usually have coordinate workbooks in which students plot the given coordinates and end up with a picture of an object or a character. These can be fun for students. Try using scrap pieces of wood and sets of coordinates and have students drill holes. Make it a contest. Can students locate the exact spot for the hole to be drilled by locating its coordinate points?

Date		M	Tu	W	Th	F

Lesson Plan for Chapter 17

Robotics

Resources

Technology Today and Tomorrow
  © 1999 – Chapter 13
Experience Technology: Communication,
  Production, Transportation, Biotechnology
  © 1997 – The activity that begins
  Section 5
The New Way Things Work
  © 1998

FOCUS

Overview

Chapter 17 is devoted to robotics, the study of robots. It gives a brief historical background and details the mechanics of robotic motion and computer control. It also addresses the impacts of this technology on society.

Objectives

• Identify technological developments that led to modern robotics.
• Explain how the stepper motor is used in robotics.
• Define the work envelope.
• Explain how feedback control is used.

Tying to Previous Knowledge

Ask students if they have been to an automatic car wash. Ask them how the various mechanical parts in the car wash duplicate the job of a person washing a vehicle. Have them list the various operations and describe each mechanical device. Begin a discussion on how the car wash is controlled. How does the car wash know how long, tall, and wide the car is? Make the comparison between the car wash and industrial robots.

TEACH

Teaching Suggestions

1. **Demonstration.** Use a teach pendant or program a robotic arm to do an eye-catching procedure. Try cutting a deck of cards, striking a wooden match, or making a ham sandwich.
2. **Discussion.** Ask students how the flexibility of a robotic arm can be used in industry, business, and even at home.
3. **Background.** The robotic explosion began in Japan during the 1970s. Although predictions of entire factories run by robots have fallen short, robots have become permanent members of the work force. New applications of robotics technology include robotic assistance for medical procedures, aid and assistance for the disabled, and even software retrievers for large mainframe computers.
4. **Problem Solving.** Ask students to list and identify new uses for robotic technology. Have them categorize the uses for home, school, a local store, a movie theater, and an amusement park. Ask students to write a program for a robotic arm to brush their teeth after a meal. To do this, have them list all the steps necessary to complete the entire process.
5. **Design and Build Activity:** "A Feedback Control Game." Be sure the user cannot see over the barrier directly onto the tracing sheet. The image must be viewed as a reflective image from the mirror. The students might experiment with the mirrors reflecting the images a few times before the observer sees it. Have the students design fold-away cases for the game.
6. **Careers.** Have students complete **Career Activity 17.** (Reproducible Career Activity masters and an Answer Key are in Part IV of this teacher's resource guide.) Students will

(continued next page)

need to look in the *Occupational Outlook Handbook,* either in print form or on the Internet. On the Internet, the URL is http://stats.bls.gov/ocohome.htm. Once at the site, students can do a keyword search for the desired career.

Answer to "Linking to Mathematics"

• Answers will vary.

Answers to "Check Your Facts"

1. Robots simulate many human functions. They move, sense their surroundings, and respond to changes in the environment.
2. Mechanical linkages to transfer power, computers to program instructions for the robot, and sensors to provide feedback to the computer had to be made before computer control robotics could become a reality.
3. Robotic arms use flexible joints to achieve degrees of freedom.
4. Stepper motors can be programmed to move very precisely, one degree or part of a degree at a time, if needed. This precise control makes the robotic arm more accurate than the human hand.
5. The work envelope is the space within which the robotic arm moves.
6. Robotic end effectors may include tool ends, welding heads, magnetic pickups, mechanical pickups, suction pickups, and spray gun heads.
7. Software can be used to program or direct a robot through a task. Teach pendants are also used to teach the robot a particular routine directly.
8. Feedback control simulates human nerves sending information back and forth from the brain to an appendage. Sensors send information about the environment and position of the robotic arm to the computer. The computer adjusts the position of the arm if needed.

ASSESS
Meeting Chapter Objectives

Have students complete **Chapter Review 17.** (Reproducible Chapter Review masters and an Answer Key are in Part IV of this teacher's resource guide.)

Evaluate

Have students complete **Chapter Test 17.** (Reproducible Chapter Test masters and an Answer Key are in Part IV of this teacher's resource guide.)

Reteach

Students may have difficulty understanding the computer language used to program robots. At this level, writing programs may not be appropriate. Try having students develop a simple pictorial program consisting of icons that can instruct a person to perform a task without using words.

Enrich

Have students research the use of robots in the operating room. Students can design new types of end effectors to accomplish specialized tasks. Have them model these end effectors. Using Legos or other modeling systems, have students build model robotic machines for specific tasks.

CLOSE

Have students complete the **Apply What You've Learned Activity:** "Design and Build a Pneumatic Control Device." This activity will take seven to ten days to complete. Have students investigate different ways of harnessing the energy from an expanding balloon. Placing the balloon in an enclosed container is the best way to control the expansion of the balloon. A piston-like device placed on top of the balloon creates linear motion.

Date		M	Tu	W	Th	F

Lesson Plan for Chapter 18

Lasers and Fiber Optics

Resources

Technology Today and Tomorrow
© 1999 – Look at the entries under
"Laser" in the index
Introduction to Technology
© 1999 – Chapter 9
Glencoe Physical Science
© 1997 – Chapter 20

FOCUS

Overview

Chapter 18 covers the characteristics of laser light and how a laser works. Uses of lasers in communication, manufacturing, construction, medicine, and business are discussed.

Objectives

- Tell what the term *laser* stands for.
- Explain the difference between laser light and ordinary light.
- Describe how a laser works.
- Identify uses for lasers in communication, manufacturing, construction, medicine, and business.

Tying to Previous Knowledge

Holographic art is becoming a common site at malls and shopping centers around the United States. Ask students if they have seen displays of holographic or "three-dimensional" art at a local mall. How is it different from traditional art? Explain that it is created with laser technology. The holographic art displayed in stores is meant for entertainment purposes only. Ask students if they can think of other, more serious, uses for holographs.

TEACH

Teaching Suggestions

1. **Demonstration.** Show that laser light does not spread out very much over distance. Hold a sheet of glossy white paper 1′ from the laser beam and have students continue to observe as the paper is moved farther away. Caution students not to look directly into the laser beam.
2. **Discussion.** Ask students to describe where they have seen lasers in use. Why are they used? Are there disadvantages to these uses? (There is concern that some store clerks may develop repetitive motion injuries from the repeated movement of products over the laser scanner at checkout counters.)
3. **Background.** Today, laser systems are commonly used in the construction industry. Arrange a visit by a local contractor to demonstrate use of traditional and laser leveling systems.
4. **Reinforcement.** Review the role of students in maintaining a safe environment in the technology laboratory. Be sure to remind students to follow all the safety precautions that accompany the laser used in class.
5. **Design and Build Activity: "A Prism System."** This activity will take one day. Students will duplicate an experiment performed by Isaac Newton in 1666 and compare the characteristics of laser light and ordinary light.
6. **Design and Build Activity: "A Light-Carrying Device."** This activity will take one day. During the activity, students will test a variety of materials to determine which can transmit light. In addition, students will determine how bending fiber optic cable affects its ability to transmit light.

(continued next page)

7. **Careers.** Have students complete **Career Activity 18.** (Reproducible Career Activity masters and an Answer Key are in Part IV of this teacher's resource guide.) Students will need to look in the *Occupational Outlook Handbook,* either in print form or on the Internet. On the Internet, the URL is http://stats.bls.gov/ocohome.htm. Once at the site, students can do a keyword search for the desired career.

Answers to "Linking to Mathematics"
- 4 suits
- 125 bolts
- 2,000 suits
- 500 bolts

Answers to "Check Your Facts"
1. The term *laser* stands for "light amplification by stimulated emission of radiation."
2. Laser light is monochromatic, directional, coherent, and bright.
3. Laser light is of one color and travels in one direction.
4. Class II helium-neon lasers are usually used in technology education class activities.
5. Communication—fiber optics and holography; manufacturing—measuring, drilling, welding; construction—measuring, aligning pipes and tunnels, checking the straightness of ceilings and walls; medicine—surgery, opening clogged arteries, drilling and cleaning teeth; business—supermarket checkouts, laser printers, credit card authentication, checking aircraft and nuclear power plant parts for hidden cracks.
6. Lasers can be used to drill, cut, weld, and heat-treat materials.
7. Advantages of laser surgery include less blood loss and less patient discomfort.

ASSESS
Meeting Chapter Objectives
Have students complete **Chapter Review 18.** (Reproducible Chapter Review masters and an Answer Key are in Part IV of this teacher's resource guide.)

Evaluate
Have students complete **Chapter Test 18.** (Reproducible Chapter Test masters and an Answer Key are in Part IV of this teacher's resource guide.)

Reteach
Some students may have difficulty remembering how laser light and ordinary light are different. Review key terms, including *coherent light, directional light,* and *monochromatic light.*

Enrich
Students who finish early or need a more challenging activity can set up a series of mirrors to direct a beam of laser light around an obstacle.

CLOSE
Have students complete the **Apply What You've Learned Activity:** "Design and Build a Light Bender." This activity will take one day and will show that a stream of water can transmit light. It will help students understand how a curved fiber optic cable can transmit light.

Date		M	Tu	W	Th	F

Lesson Plan for Chapter 19

Engineering

Resources

Introduction to Technology
© 1999 – Chapter 1
Technology Today and Tomorrow
© 1999 – Look at the entries under "Engineering" in the index.

FOCUS

Overview

Chapter 19 explores the field of engineering. It focuses on the many different types of engineering and the engineering process. A thematic example is given showing how the different fields of engineering work together to solve a common problem.

Objectives

- Describe the basic job of an engineer.
- Discuss the specific jobs performed by different types of engineers.
- Identify and explain the basic steps in the engineering process.

Tying to Previous Knowledge

Ask students if they remember building shelters at home from pillows, blankets, chairs, and any other materials available. Have them describe some of their best structures. What materials did they use? Explain that they were, even as young children, playing "engineer." They were using their knowledge and imagination to develop designs for shelters.

TEACH

Teaching Suggestions

1. **Demonstration.** Give each student a 12″ length of 14-gauge aluminum wire. Ask students to design and model a new style of paper clip that will keep fifteen envelopes together even after falling off a desk. Ask students to record the steps in the design process they used.

2. **Discussion.** Discuss the process students used to design the paper clip. Did they use trial and error, or did they have a design concept from the start of the activity? Ask students if they developed new ideas as they viewed their classmates' ideas. What innovations might they make to a classmate's design? What problems did they encounter with the material or forming the materials?

3. **Reinforcement.** Review the design or engineering process with the students. Discuss each step and the need for it. Have students share their designs with the class for the second time. Discuss whether the process helped generate new and better ideas.

4. **Problem Solving.** Have students practice idea-generating techniques such as brainstorming, sketching, and forced connections. Use the following problem: A sporting shoe store has collected hundreds of old sneakers and sports shoes. Develop a product or use for these throwaways.

5. **Design and Build Activity:** "A Jack-in-the-Box." This activity will take several weeks to complete. Background information on simple machines and cam action will be helpful to students. Have students explore latch systems used on everyday items such as cabinets and appliances. To save time, cardboard boxes such as shoe boxes and cereal boxes can be used as the container for the mechanism. Other than a spring, what else might be used to release energy quickly?

6. **Design and Build Activity:** "A Shelf for a School Locker." Many commercial versions of this product are available. Have students locate some examples and evaluate them for size, assembly, and materials. Some designs

(continued next page)

will have to be assembled while in the locker. Cardboard and paper models will be helpful for testing and gathering data about designs that unfold in the locker. Have students investigate modular designs that can be used for multi-level shelving.

7. **Careers.** Have students complete **Career Activity 19.** (Reproducible Career Activity masters and an Answer Key are in Part IV of this teacher's resource guide.) Students will need to look in the *Occupational Outlook Handbook,* either in print form or on the Internet. On the Internet, the URL is http://stats.bls.gov/ocohome.htm. Once at the site, students can do a keyword search for the desired career.

Answers to "Linking to Mathematics"

- 6 inches

Answers to "Check Your Facts"

1. They develop and improve product designs.
2. Mechanical engineers design and improve machines and machine parts. Structural engineers work with architects to ensure the strength and integrity of a structure. Electronic engineers develop circuits to control electron flow.
3. Mechanical engineers develop delivery systems for vending machines.
4. Electrical engineers determine the power requirements for a portable radio.
5. First the engineer identifies a problem or need that requires a solution. The engineer then identifies the criteria or specifications for the solution. Next, the engineer researches and gathers information related to the design problem. This leads to the next step of developing possible design solutions. After picking the best solution, the engineer models the solution, tests it, and evaluates it for the final design.
6. Engineers develop many solutions so they can "optimize" or pick the one solution that meets the criteria defined earlier in the engineering process.
7. A trade-off is giving up one design feature to make another feature possible. For example,

a better material may be available for a product, but using it would exceed the budget for the product. The engineer can choose to stay within budget or use the better material, but not both.

8. Engineers often use trade magazines and books as resources to find information about a particular design problem.

ASSESS
Meeting Chapter Objectives

Have students complete **Chapter Review 19.** (Reproducible Chapter Review masters and an Answer Key are in Part IV of this teacher's resource guide.)

Evaluate

Have students complete **Chapter Test 19.** (Reproducible Chapter Test masters and an Answer Key are in Part IV of this teacher's resource guide.)

Reteach

Can the engineering process be used to solve problems that are not technical? Have students try to use the technique to solve a social problem, such as teenage smoking or watching too much television.

Enrich

For those students who need a more challenging activity, have them design an electrically activated Jack-in-the-box. Students can focus on relays, electromagnets, and solenoids.

CLOSE

Have students complete the **Apply What You've Learned Activity:** "Design and Build a Toothpick Dispenser." This activity will take several weeks. Have students investigate commercial dispensers available. Students can make paper models to test design solutions. Some toothpick shapes make the problem harder to solve. Round toothpicks are easier. Have students prepare detailed drawings before they build.

Date		M	Tu	W	Th	F

Lesson Plan for Chapter 20

Applied Physics

Resources

Glencoe Physical Science
  © 1997 – This is a tremendous resource for applied physics.
The New Way Things Work
  © 1998
Visual Dictionary of Physics
  © 1995

FOCUS

Overview

Chapter 20 shows the relationship between technology and science by providing examples of the application of scientific theory in technological products.

Objectives

- List the steps in the scientific method.
- Define the term *applied physics*.
- Explain the forces that are involved in motion.
- State and explain each of Newton's three laws of motion.
- Explain the difference between work and power.
- Explain how sound and light waves are different.

Tying to Previous Knowledge

Why do you wear sneakers or sports shoes when you play sports? Allow students to think about the question and then have them explain their answers. Then focus the conversation on the friction that the soft bottom of the shoe provides. How does this energy-robbing force benefit the student while playing basketball or volleyball?

TEACH

Teaching Suggestions

1. **Demonstration.** Set up a slanted board covered with 100-grit abrasive paper. Attach a spring scale to a sneaker and drag it up the rough surface. Record the force needed to move the sneaker up the board. Remove the abrasive paper and repeat the experiment on the smooth board surface. Ask students to explain why the two surfaces require different forces to move the sneaker up the incline. What force caused the difference?

2. **Reinforcement.** In-line skating is the current sporting rage across the country. Ask students to list and show how the laws of physics govern how the skate and skater move. Example: Momentum keeps a person rolling down the sidewalk. The same law explains why you might fall on your face when your skate hits a small stone.

3. **Design and Build Activity: "A Crane."** Cranes come in many sizes and have many load capacities. The selection of the right crane size and capacity for a job is vital if work is to be done safely and efficiently. This activity allows students to apply both the theoretical and mathematical aspects of many laws of physics. Focus lessons on simple machines, mechanical advantage, and the structural integrity of the crane. Try using spring scales to evaluate the lifting force of the cranes.

4. **Design and Build Activity: "A Sound Wave Tester."** Before the laws of physics can be incorporated into a technological design, they must be understood. This is usually accomplished through experimentation. This activity allows students to conduct an experiment, gather data, and draw conclusions. Start the activity by teaching the scientific method. Ask a science colleague for

(continued next page)

assistance. This activity should only take one or two class periods. Consider doing it as a demonstration and leading a discussion in class focused on the results of the experiment.

5. **Careers.** Have students complete **Career Activity 20.** (Reproducible Career Activity masters and an Answer Key are in Part IV of this teacher's resource guide.) Students will need to look in the *Occupational Outlook Handbook,* either in print form or on the Internet. On the Internet, the URL is http://stats.bls.gov/ocohome.htm. Once at the site, students can do a keyword search for the desired career.

Answer to "Linking to Mathematics"

- 2 hp

Answers to "Check Your Facts"

1. State the problem, gather information, form a hypothesis, perform experiment, record and analyze data, and state conclusion.
2. Applied physics is the study of how objects are moved, the forces that move them, and the resulting work accomplished.
3. A force can place an object in motion. Friction opposes motion and can cause an object to slow down and even stop. Gravity can place an object in motion or cause an object to slow or even change direction.
4. The three types of friction are surface friction, rolling friction, and fluid friction.
5. The gravitational force acting on objects depends on the size of the objects and the distance between them.
6. First law: An object at rest will stay at rest and an object in motion will stay in motion, unless an outside force acts upon it. Second law: The rate at which an object moves depends upon its mass and the force acting on it. Third law: All forces occur in pairs. For every action there is an equal and opposite reaction.
7. Work takes place when an applied force causes an object to move. Power is the amount of work done in a certain period of time.
8. Mechanical advantage is the number of times a machine multiplies a force.
9. Unlike light waves, sound waves need a medium to flow through, such as air or water.
10. A photon is a packet or bundle of light energy.

ASSESS

Meeting Chapter Objectives

Have students complete **Chapter Review 20.** (Reproducible Chapter Review masters and an Answer Key are in Part IV of this teacher's resource guide.)

Evaluate

Have students complete **Chapter Test 20.** (Reproducible Chapter Test masters and an Answer Key are in Part IV of this teacher's resource guide.)

Reteach

Students have difficulty understanding abstract theories. It is important to show everyday examples of applied physics in action. For example, demonstrate action/reaction in the following way: Have a student sit straight up in a chair at the front of the room. Have the rest of the class focus on the back, head, and neck of the student in the chair. *Gently* kick the back bottom support of the chair, applying a forward force. Ask students "In what direction did the student's head move?" In an auto accident, this is called whiplash. How do auto manufacturers help prevent whiplash in a car?

Enrich

Students who finish early can build a model of a concert hall using the information they learned about sound energy. Require them to make it acoustically correct, using modeling materials to set up baffles and reflective surfaces to control the sound in the hall.

CLOSE

Have students complete the **Apply What You've Learned Activity:** "Design and Build a 'Reaction' Rocket Racer." This activity should take four to eight periods. Be sure students apply both the scientific method and the engineering method to design and gather data about their racers. Have students consider variables such as wheel diameter, weight, number of wheels, angle of the straw, and friction between the wheel and axle. Try having each team focus on one factor and share their results.

Reproducibles

The Reproducibles part of this TRG includes one Career Activity Master for each textbook chapter, one Chapter Review for each textbook chapter, and one Chapter Test for each textbook chapter. An answer key for each type of reproducible begins on page **245**.

Investigate a Career

The careers below are all related to technology. Select one career to investigate. Circle or highlight the name of that career.

Industrial Production Manager	Computer Scientist/ Systems Analyst	Data Processing Manager	Engineering Manager
Industrial Engineering Technician	Operations Manager	Construction and Building Inspector	Biological Scientist

For the career you selected, look in the *Occupational Outlook Handbook* and complete the following.

1. **Nature of the Work.** Name three things a person does in that career. _____

    _____

    _____

2. **Employment.** About how many people have this career? _____

    _____

    For what industry (or industries) do they work? _____

    _____

3. **Training.** What is the minimum training or education needed for an entry-level job in this career?

    _____ apprenticeship   _____ bachelor's degree

    _____ associate degree   _____ master's degree

    _____ other (explain) _____

4. **Job Outlook.** How does the job outlook for this career compare to the average of all occupations?

    _____ growth will be faster than average

    _____ growth will be the same as the average

    _____ growth will be slower than average

(continued next page)

Career Activity 1 (continued)

5. **Earnings.** What is the median salary? (If median salary is not available, list the starting salary instead.) _____

_____

What do YOU think?

Name two things you would enjoy about this career. Tell why.

_____

_____

_____

Name two things you think would be difficult about this career. Tell why.

_____

_____

_____

What have you learned in Chapter 1 that applies to this career?

_____

_____

_____

TECHNOLOGY INTERACTIONS Teacher's Resource Guide

Investigate a Career

The careers below are all related to design and problem solving technologies. Select one career to investigate. Circle or highlight the name of that career.

Urban and Regional Planner	Marketing Research Analyst	Systems Analyst
Consumer Safety	Engineer	Industrial Designer

For the career you selected, look in the *Occupational Outlook Handbook* and complete the following.

1. **Nature of the Work.** Name three things a person does in that career. _____

   _____

   _____

2. **Employment.** About how many people have this career? _____

   _____

   For what industry (or industries) do they work? _____

   _____

3. **Training.** What is the minimum training or education needed for an entry-level job in this career?

   _____ apprenticeship   _____ bachelor's degree

   _____ associate degree   _____ master's degree

   _____ other (explain) _____

4. **Job Outlook.** How does the job outlook for this career compare to the average of all occupations?

   _____ growth will be faster than average

   _____ growth will be the same as the average

   _____ growth will be slower than average

(continued next page)

Career Activity 2 (continued)

5. **Earnings.** What is the median salary? (If median salary is not available, list the starting salary instead.) _____

_____

What do YOU think?

Name two things you would enjoy about this career. Tell why.

_____
_____
_____

Name two things you think would be difficult about this career. Tell why.

_____
_____
_____

What have you learned in Chapter 2 that applies to this career?

_____
_____
_____

Investigate a Career

The careers below are all related to drafting and CAD technologies. Select one career to investigate. Circle or highlight the name of that career.

Architect	Electronics Engineer	Drafter
Electrical Drafter	Engineering Technician	Tool Programmer

For the career you selected, look in the *Occupational Outlook Handbook* and complete the following.

1. **Nature of the Work.** Name three things a person does in that career. _____

    _____

    _____

2. **Employment.** About how many people have this career? _____

    _____

    For what industry (or industries) do they work? _____

    _____

3. **Training.** What is the minimum training or education needed for an entry-level job in this career?

    _____ apprenticeship   _____ bachelor's degree

    _____ associate degree   _____ master's degree

    _____ other (explain) _____

4. **Job Outlook.** How does the job outlook for this career compare to the average of all occupations?

    _____ growth will be faster than average

    _____ growth will be the same as the average

    _____ growth will be slower than average

(continued next page)

Career Activity 3 (continued)

5. **Earnings.** What is the median salary? (If median salary is not available, list the starting salary instead.) _____

_____

What do YOU think?

Name two things you would enjoy about this career. Tell why.

_____

_____

_____

_____

Name two things you think would be difficult about this career. Tell why.

_____

_____

_____

_____

What have you learned in Chapter 3 that applies to this career?

_____

_____

_____

_____

Name _____ Class _____ Date _____

Investigate a Career

The careers below are all related to desktop publishing. Select one career to investigate. Circle or highlight the name of that career.

Graphic Artist	Writer/Editor	Photographer	Word Processor

For the career you selected, look in the *Occupational Outlook Handbook* and complete the following.

1. **Nature of the Work.** Name three things a person does in that career. _____

   _____

   _____

2. **Employment.** About how many people have this career? _____

   _____

   For what industry (or industries) do they work? _____

   _____

3. **Training.** What is the minimum training or education needed for an entry-level job in this career?

   _____ apprenticeship   _____ bachelor's degree

   _____ associate degree   _____ master's degree

   _____ other (explain) _____

4. **Job Outlook.** How does the job outlook for this career compare to the average of all occupations?

   _____ growth will be faster than average

   _____ growth will be the same as the average

   _____ growth will be slower than average

(continued next page)

Career Activity 4 (continued)

5. **Earnings.** What is the median salary? (If median salary is not available, list the starting salary instead.) _____

_____

What do YOU think?

Name two things you would enjoy about this career. Tell why.

_____

_____

_____

_____

Name two things you think would be difficult about this career. Tell why.

_____

_____

_____

_____

What have you learned in Chapter 4 that applies to this career?

_____

_____

_____

_____

TECHNOLOGY INTERACTIONS Teacher's Resource Guide

Investigate a Career

The careers below are all related to computer animation technologies. Select one career to investigate. Circle or highlight the name of that career.

Animator	Illustrator	Computer Programmer	Computer Scientist

For the career you selected, look in the *Occupational Outlook Handbook* and complete the following.

1. **Nature of the Work.** Name three things a person does in that career. _____

   _____

   _____

2. **Employment.** About how many people have this career? _____

   _____

   For what industry (or industries) do they work? _____

   _____

3. **Training.** What is the minimum training or education needed for an entry-level job in this career?

   _____ apprenticeship   _____ bachelor's degree

   _____ associate degree   _____ master's degree

   _____ other (explain) _____

4. **Job Outlook.** How does the job outlook for this career compare to the average of all occupations?

   _____ growth will be faster than average

   _____ growth will be the same as the average

   _____ growth will be slower than average

(continued next page)

Career Activity 5 (continued)

5. **Earnings.** What is the median salary? (If median salary is not available, list the starting salary instead.) _____

_____

What do YOU think?

Name two things you would enjoy about this career. Tell why.

_____

_____

_____

Name two things you think would be difficult about this career. Tell why.

_____

_____

_____

What have you learned in Chapter 5 that applies to this career?

_____

_____

_____

TECHNOLOGY INTERACTIONS Teacher's Resource Guide

Investigate a Career

The careers below are all related to the Internet. Select one career to investigate. Circle or highlight the name of that career.

Librarian/Media Specialist	Library Technician/Media Assistant	Computer Programmer
Database Administrator	Computer Support Analyst	Service/Sales Representative

For the career you selected, look in the *Occupational Outlook Handbook* and complete the following.

1. **Nature of the Work.** Name three things a person does in that career. _____

   _____

   _____

2. **Employment.** About how many people have this career? _____

   _____

   For what industry (or industries) do they work? _____

   _____

3. **Training.** What is the minimum training or education needed for an entry-level job in this career?

   _____ apprenticeship   _____ bachelor's degree

   _____ associate degree   _____ master's degree

   _____ other (explain) _____

4. **Job Outlook.** How does the job outlook for this career compare to the average of all occupations?

   _____ growth will be faster than average

   _____ growth will be the same as the average

   _____ growth will be slower than average

(continued next page)

Career Activity 6 (continued)

5. **Earnings.** What is the median salary? (If median salary is not available, list the starting salary instead.) _____

_____

What do YOU think?

Name two things you would enjoy about this career. Tell why.

_____

_____

_____

_____

Name two things you think would be difficult about this career. Tell why.

_____

_____

_____

_____

What have you learned in Chapter 6 that applies to this career?

_____

_____

_____

_____

TECHNOLOGY INTERACTIONS Teacher's Resource Guide

Investigate a Career

The careers below are all related to audio/video production and multimedia. Select one career to investigate. Circle or highlight the name of that career.

Broadcast Technician	Recording Engineer	Sound Mixer
Camera Operator	Reporter	Announcer

For the career you selected, look in the *Occupational Outlook Handbook* and complete the following.

1. **Nature of the Work.** Name three things a person does in that career. _____

   _____

   _____

2. **Employment.** About how many people have this career? _____

   _____

   For what industry (or industries) do they work? _____

   _____

3. **Training.** What is the minimum training or education needed for an entry-level job in this career?

   _____ apprenticeship   _____ bachelor's degree

   _____ associate degree   _____ master's degree

   _____ other (explain) _____

4. **Job Outlook.** How does the job outlook for this career compare to the average of all occupations?

   _____ growth will be faster than average

   _____ growth will be the same as the average

   _____ growth will be slower than average

(continued next page)

Career Activity 7 (continued)

5. **Earnings.** What is the median salary? (If median salary is not available, list the starting salary instead.) _____

_____

What do YOU think?

Name two things you would enjoy about this career. Tell why.

_____

_____

_____

_____

Name two things you think would be difficult about this career. Tell why.

_____

_____

_____

_____

What have you learned in Chapter 7 that applies to this career?

_____

_____

_____

_____

TECHNOLOGY INTERACTIONS Teacher's Resource Guide

Name _____ Class _____ Date _____

Investigate a Career

The careers below are all related to manufacturing. Select one career to investigate. Circle or highlight the name of that career.

Industrial Engineer	Mechanical Engineer	Industrial Production Manager
Occupational Safety and Health Inspector	Industrial Buyer	Industrial Machinery Repairer

For the career you selected, look in the *Occupational Outlook Handbook* and complete the following.

1. **Nature of the Work.** Name three things a person does in that career. _____

   _____

   _____

2. **Employment.** About how many people have this career? _____

   _____

   For what industry (or industries) do they work? _____

   _____

3. **Training.** What is the minimum training or education needed for an entry-level job in this career?

   _____ apprenticeship   _____ bachelor's degree

   _____ associate degree   _____ master's degree

   _____ other (explain) _____

4. **Job Outlook.** How does the job outlook for this career compare to the average of all occupations?

   _____ growth will be faster than average

   _____ growth will be the same as the average

   _____ growth will be slower than average

(continued next page)

Name _____ **Class** _____ **Date** _____

Career Activity 8 (continued)

5. **Earnings.** What is the median salary? (If median salary is not available, list the starting salary instead.) _____

_____

What do YOU think?

Name two things you would enjoy about this career. Tell why.

_____

_____

_____

_____

Name two things you think would be difficult about this career. Tell why.

_____

_____

_____

_____

What have you learned in Chapter 8 that applies to this career?

_____

_____

_____

_____

120

TECHNOLOGY INTERACTIONS Teacher's Resource Guide
Copyright © Glencoe/McGraw-Hill

Investigate a Career

The careers below are all related to structure production technologies. Select one career to investigate. Circle or highlight the name of that career.

Architect	Civil Engineering Technician	Construction Manager	Construction and Building Inspector
Cost Estimator	Electrician	Survey Technician	Interior Designer

For the career you selected, look in the *Occupational Outlook Handbook* and complete the following.

1. **Nature of the Work.** Name three things a person does in that career. _____

   _____

   _____

2. **Employment.** About how many people have this career? _____

   _____

   For what industry (or industries) do they work? _____

   _____

3. **Training.** What is the minimum training or education needed for an entry-level job in this career?

   _____ apprenticeship   _____ bachelor's degree

   _____ associate degree   _____ master's degree

   _____ other (explain) _____

4. **Job Outlook.** How does the job outlook for this career compare to the average of all occupations?

   _____ growth will be faster than average

   _____ growth will be the same as the average

   _____ growth will be slower than average

(continued next page)

Career Activity 9 (continued)

5. **Earnings.** What is the median salary? (If median salary is not available, list the starting salary instead.) _____

_____

What do YOU think?

Name two things you would enjoy about this career. Tell why.

_____

_____

_____

_____

Name two things you think would be difficult about this career. Tell why.

_____

_____

_____

_____

What have you learned in Chapter 9 that applies to this career?

_____

_____

_____

_____

Investigate a Career

The careers below are all related to flight technologies. Select one career to investigate. Circle or highlight the name of that career.

Pilot	Air Traffic Controller	Aerospace Engineer	Aircraft Mechanic
Aviation Safety Inspector	Precision Assembler	Reservation Ticket Agent	Flight Attendant

For the career you selected, look in the *Occupational Outlook Handbook* and complete the following.

1. **Nature of the Work.** Name three things a person does in that career. _____

    _____

    _____

2. **Employment.** About how many people have this career? _____

    _____

    For what industry (or industries) do they work? _____

    _____

3. **Training.** What is the minimum training or education needed for an entry-level job in this career?

    _____ apprenticeship   _____ bachelor's degree

    _____ associate degree   _____ master's degree

    _____ other (explain) _____

4. **Job Outlook.** How does the job outlook for this career compare to the average of all occupations?

    _____ growth will be faster than average

    _____ growth will be the same as the average

    _____ growth will be slower than average

(continued next page)

Career Activity 10 (continued)

5. **Earnings.** What is the median salary? (If median salary is not available, list the starting salary instead.) _____

_____

What do YOU think?

Name two things you would enjoy about this career. Tell why.

_____

_____

_____

_____

Name two things you think would be difficult about this career. Tell why.

_____

_____

_____

_____

What have you learned in Chapter 10 that applies to this career?

_____

_____

_____

_____

Investigate a Career

The careers below are all related to land or water transportation. Select one career to investigate. Circle or highlight the name of that career.

Marine Engineer	Rail Engineer	Diesel Mechanic
Automotive Mechanic	Customs Inspector	Travel Agent

For the career you selected, look in the *Occupational Outlook Handbook* and complete the following.

1. **Nature of the Work.** Name three things a person does in that career. _____

   _____

   _____

2. **Employment.** About how many people have this career? _____

   _____

   For what industry (or industries) do they work? _____

   _____

3. **Training.** What is the minimum training or education needed for an entry-level job in this career?

   _____ apprenticeship   _____ bachelor's degree

   _____ associate degree   _____ master's degree

   _____ other (explain) _____

4. **Job Outlook.** How does the job outlook for this career compare to the average of all occupations?

   _____ growth will be faster than average

   _____ growth will be the same as the average

   _____ growth will be slower than average

(continued next page)

Career Activity 11 (continued)

5. **Earnings.** What is the median salary? (If median salary is not available, list the starting salary instead.) _____

_____

What do YOU think?

Name two things you would enjoy about this career. Tell why.

_____

_____

_____

Name two things you think would be difficult about this career. Tell why.

_____

_____

_____

What have you learned in Chapter 11 that applies to this career?

_____

_____

_____

TECHNOLOGY INTERACTIONS Teacher's Resource Guide

Name _____ Class _____ Date _____

Investigate a Career

The careers below are all related to fluid power technologies. Select one career to investigate. Circle or highlight the name of that career.

Stationary Engineer	**Water and Wastewater Treatment Plant Operator**	**Nuclear Engineer**
Petroleum Engineer	**Petroleum Technician**	**Mobile Heavy Equipment Mechanic**

For the career you selected, look in the *Occupational Outlook Handbook* and complete the following.

1. **Nature of the Work.** Name three things a person does in that career. _____

   _____

   _____

2. **Employment.** About how many people have this career? _____

   _____

   For what industry (or industries) do they work? _____

   _____

3. **Training.** What is the minimum training or education needed for an entry-level job in this career?

   _____ apprenticeship   _____ bachelor's degree

   _____ associate degree   _____ master's degree

   _____ other (explain) _____

4. **Job Outlook.** How does the job outlook for this career compare to the average of all occupations?

   _____ growth will be faster than average

   _____ growth will be the same as the average

   _____ growth will be slower than average

(continued next page)

Career Activity 12 (continued)

5. **Earnings.** What is the median salary? (If median salary is not available, list the starting salary instead.) _____

_____

What do YOU think?

Name two things you would enjoy about this career. Tell why.

_____

_____

_____

_____

Name two things you think would be difficult about this career. Tell why.

_____

_____

_____

_____

What have you learned in Chapter 12 that applies to this career?

_____

_____

_____

_____

Investigate a Career

The careers below are all related to health technologies. Select one career to investigate. Circle or highlight the name of that career.

Physician	Medical Scientist	Biochemist	Medical Technologist
Physical Therapist	Cardiovascular Technologist	Medical Records Technician	Licensed Practical Nurse

For the career you selected, look in the *Occupational Outlook Handbook* and complete the following.

1. **Nature of the Work.** Name three things a person does in that career. _____

   _____

   _____

2. **Employment.** About how many people have this career? _____

   _____

   For what industry (or industries) do they work? _____

   _____

3. **Training.** What is the minimum training or education needed for an entry-level job in this career?

   _____ apprenticeship   _____ bachelor's degree

   _____ associate degree   _____ master's degree

   _____ other (explain) _____

4. **Job Outlook.** How does the job outlook for this career compare to the average of all occupations?

   _____ growth will be faster than average

   _____ growth will be the same as the average

   _____ growth will be slower than average

(continued next page)

Career Activity 13 (continued)

5. **Earnings.** What is the median salary? (If median salary is not available, list the starting salary instead.) _____

_____

What do YOU think?

Name two things you would enjoy about this career. Tell why.

_____

_____

_____

Name two things you think would be difficult about this career. Tell why.

_____

_____

_____

What have you learned in Chapter 13 that applies to this career?

_____

_____

_____

_____

TECHNOLOGY INTERACTIONS Teacher's Resource Guide

Name _____ Class _____ Date _____

Investigate a Career

The careers below are all related to environmental technologies. Select one career to investigate. Circle or highlight the name of that career.

Biological Scientist	Geologist	Forester
Groundskeeper	Landscape Architect	Farm Operator

For the career you selected, look in the *Occupational Outlook Handbook* and complete the following.

1. **Nature of the Work.** Name three things a person does in that career. _____

   _____

   _____

2. **Employment.** About how many people have this career? _____

   _____

   For what industry (or industries) do they work? _____

   _____

3. **Training.** What is the minimum training or education needed for an entry-level job in this career?

   _____ apprenticeship   _____ bachelor's degree

   _____ associate degree   _____ master's degree

   _____ other (explain) _____

4. **Job Outlook.** How does the job outlook for this career compare to the average of all occupations?

   _____ growth will be faster than average

   _____ growth will be the same as the average

   _____ growth will be slower than average

(continued next page)

TECHNOLOGY INTERACTIONS Teacher's Resource Guide
Copyright © Glencoe/McGraw-Hill

Career Activity 14 (continued)

5. **Earnings.** What is the median salary? (If median salary is not available, list the starting salary instead.) _____

_____

What do YOU think?

Name two things you would enjoy about this career. Tell why.

_____

_____

_____

Name two things you think would be difficult about this career. Tell why.

_____

_____

_____

What have you learned in Chapter 14 that applies to this career?

_____

_____

_____

Investigate a Career

The careers below are all related to electricity and electronics. Select one career to investigate. Circle or highlight the name of that career.

Electrical and Electronics Engineer	Electronic Equipment Repairer	Industrial Electronics Technician
Computer/Office Machine Service Technician	Electrician	Electronic Semiconductor Processor

For the career you selected, look in the *Occupational Outlook Handbook* and complete the following.

1. **Nature of the Work.** Name three things a person does in that career. _____

   _____

   _____

2. **Employment.** About how many people have this career? _____

   _____

   For what industry (or industries) do they work? _____

   _____

3. **Training.** What is the minimum training or education needed for an entry-level job in this career?

   _____ apprenticeship   _____ bachelor's degree

   _____ associate degree   _____ master's degree

   _____ other (explain) _____

4. **Job Outlook.** How does the job outlook for this career compare to the average of all occupations?

   _____ growth will be faster than average

   _____ growth will be the same as the average

   _____ growth will be slower than average

(continued next page)

Career Activity 15 (continued)

5. **Earnings.** What is the median salary? (If median salary is not available, list the starting salary instead.) _____

_____

What do YOU think?

Name two things you would enjoy about this career. Tell why.

_____

_____

_____

_____

Name two things you think would be difficult about this career. Tell why.

_____

_____

_____

_____

What have you learned in Chapter 15 that applies to this career?

_____

_____

_____

_____

Name _____ Class _____ Date _____

Investigate a Career

The careers below are all related to computer control systems. Select one career to investigate. Circle or highlight the name of that career.

Tool Programmer	Machinist	Metal- and Plastics-Working Machine Operator	Tool and Die Makers

For the career you selected, look in the *Occupational Outlook Handbook* and complete the following.

1. **Nature of the Work.** Name three things a person does in that career. _____

   _____

   _____

2. **Employment.** About how many people have this career? _____

   _____

   For what industry (or industries) do they work? _____

   _____

3. **Training.** What is the minimum training or education needed for an entry-level job in this career?

   _____ apprenticeship   _____ bachelor's degree

   _____ associate degree   _____ master's degree

   _____ other (explain) _____

4. **Job Outlook.** How does the job outlook for this career compare to the average of all occupations?

   _____ growth will be faster than average

   _____ growth will be the same as the average

   _____ growth will be slower than average

(continued next page)

Career Activity 16 (continued)

5. **Earnings.** What is the median salary? (If median salary is not available, list the starting salary instead.) _____

_____

What do YOU think?

Name two things you would enjoy about this career. Tell why.

_____

_____

_____

_____

Name two things you think would be difficult about this career. Tell why.

_____

_____

_____

_____

What have you learned in Chapter 16 that applies to this career?

_____

_____

_____

_____

TECHNOLOGY INTERACTIONS Teacher's Resource Guide

Investigate a Career

The careers below are all related to robotics. Select one career to investigate. Circle or highlight the name of that career.

Mechanical Engineer	Mechanical Engineering Technician	Computer Programmer
Precision Assembler	Industrial Electronics Technician	Military Communications and Intelligence Specialist

For the career you selected, look in the *Occupational Outlook Handbook* and complete the following.

1. **Nature of the Work.** Name three things a person does in that career. _____

   _____

   _____

2. **Employment.** About how many people have this career? _____

   _____

   For what industry (or industries) do they work? _____

   _____

3. **Training.** What is the minimum training or education needed for an entry-level job in this career?

   _____ apprenticeship   _____ bachelor's degree

   _____ associate degree   _____ master's degree

   _____ other (explain) _____

4. **Job Outlook.** How does the job outlook for this career compare to the average of all occupations?

   _____ growth will be faster than average

   _____ growth will be the same as the average

   _____ growth will be slower than average

(continued next page)

5. **Earnings.** What is the median salary? (If median salary is not available, list the starting salary instead.) _____

_____

What do YOU think?

Name two things you would enjoy about this career. Tell why.

_____

_____

_____

Name two things you think would be difficult about this career. Tell why.

_____

_____

_____

What have you learned in Chapter 17 that applies to this career?

_____

_____

_____

Career Activity 18

Investigate a Career

The careers below are all related to laser and fiber optic technology. Select one career to investigate. Circle or highlight the name of that career.

Survey Technician	Physician	Aerospace Engineer
Communication Equipment Mechanic	Mechanical Engineering Technician	Military Electronic Equipment Repairers

For the career you selected, look in the *Occupational Outlook Handbook* and complete the following.

1. **Nature of the Work.** Name three things a person does in that career. _____

   _____

   _____

2. **Employment.** About how many people have this career? _____

   _____

   For what industry (or industries) do they work? _____

   _____

3. **Training.** What is the minimum training or education needed for an entry-level job in this career?

   _____ apprenticeship   _____ bachelor's degree

   _____ associate degree   _____ master's degree

   _____ other (explain) _____

4. **Job Outlook.** How does the job outlook for this career compare to the average of all occupations?

   _____ growth will be faster than average

   _____ growth will be the same as the average

   _____ growth will be slower than average

(continued next page)

5. **Earnings.** What is the median salary? (If median salary is not available, list the starting salary instead.) _____

_____

What do YOU think?

Name two things you would enjoy about this career. Tell why.

_____

_____

_____

_____

Name two things you think would be difficult about this career. Tell why.

_____

_____

_____

_____

What have you learned in Chapter 18 that applies to this career?

_____

_____

_____

_____

Name _____ Class _____ Date _____

Investigate a Career

The careers below are all related to engineering. Select one career to investigate. Circle or highlight the name of that career.

Aerospace Engineer	Chemical Engineer	Civil Engineer	Mechanical Engineer
Electrical and Electronics Engineer	Metallurgical, Ceramic, Materials Engineer	Nuclear Engineer	Computer Engineer

For the career you selected, look in the *Occupational Outlook Handbook* and complete the following.

1. **Nature of the Work.** Name three things a person does in that career. _____

   _____

   _____

2. **Employment.** About how many people have this career? _____

   _____

   For what industry (or industries) do they work? _____

   _____

3. **Training.** What is the minimum training or education needed for an entry-level job in this career?

   _____ apprenticeship   _____ bachelor's degree

   _____ associate degree   _____ master's degree

   _____ other (explain) _____

4. **Job Outlook.** How does the job outlook for this career compare to the average of all occupations?

   _____ growth will be faster than average

   _____ growth will be the same as the average

   _____ growth will be slower than average

(continued next page)

Career Activity 19 (continued)

5. **Earnings.** What is the median salary? (If median salary is not available, list the starting salary instead.) _____

_____

What do YOU think?

Name two things you would enjoy about this career. Tell why.

_____

_____

_____

_____

Name two things you think would be difficult about this career. Tell why.

_____

_____

_____

_____

What have you learned in Chapter 19 that applies to this career?

_____

_____

_____

_____

Name _____ Class _____ Date _____

Investigate a Career

The careers below are all related to physics. Select one career to investigate. Circle or highlight the name of that career.

Physicist	Geophysicist	Astronomer
College and University Faculty	Nuclear Engineer	Nuclear Science Technician

For the career you selected, look in the *Occupational Outlook Handbook* and complete the following.

1. **Nature of the Work.** Name three things a person does in that career. _____

   _____

   _____

2. **Employment.** About how many people have this career? _____

   _____

   For what industry (or industries) do they work? _____

   _____

3. **Training.** What is the minimum training or education needed for an entry-level job in this career?

   _____ apprenticeship   _____ bachelor's degree

   _____ associate degree   _____ master's degree

   _____ other (explain) _____

4. **Job Outlook.** How does the job outlook for this career compare to the average of all occupations?

   _____ growth will be faster than average

   _____ growth will be the same as the average

   _____ growth will be slower than average

(continued next page)

Career Activity 20 (continued)

5. **Earnings.** What is the median salary? (If median salary is not available, list the starting salary instead.) _____

_____

What do YOU think?

Name two things you would enjoy about this career. Tell why.

_____

_____

_____

_____

Name two things you think would be difficult about this career. Tell why.

_____

_____

_____

_____

What have you learned in Chapter 20 that applies to this career?

_____

_____

_____

_____

TECHNOLOGY INTERACTIONS Teacher's Resource Guide
Copyright © Glencoe/McGraw-Hill

Chapter Review   1

How Technology Works

I. Vocabulary Review

In the blank, write the word or words that best complete each sentence.

_____ 1. The steam engine is one of the many examples of new technologies and products invented during the _____ Age.

_____ 2. A(n) _____ is an orderly way of achieving a purpose or goal.

_____ 3. Information about the output of a system that is used to adjust a system to reach a desired goal is called _____.

_____ 4. Anything that is used to do work can be called a(n) _____.

_____ 5. _____ are all the things needed to produce a product.

_____ 6. One of the technologies used to control manufacturing processes is CIM, or _____. (3 words)

_____ 7. The _____ part of a system is the part during which something is done.

_____ 8. Complex systems can be divided into smaller units called _____.

_____ 9. The end product produced by a system is the _____ of that system.

_____ 10. _____ technologies are those that are used to make or change products using living organisms.

II. Concept/Skills Review

In the blank at the left, write the letter of the choice that best completes the statement or answers the question.

_____ 11. Which of the following is a tool of technology?
   a. food   b. shelter   c. plow   d. protection

(continued next page)

_____ 12. A person who works for a company but stays at home instead of commuting to work every day is working in a(n)
   a. electronic cottage.
   b. home electronics store.
   c. home technology center.
   d. outlet company.

_____ 13. Technology is
   a. a relationship between human needs and wants.
   b. a process of discovering more about nature.
   c. the result of industrial development.
   d. science put to practical use.

_____ 14. An example of a tool developed during the Agricultural Age is the
   a. loom.   b. sickle.   c. ax.   d. steam engine.

_____ 15. The Information Age
   a. enabled factories to satisfy consumer demand for new products.
   b. was built upon the development of the transistor and the computer.
   c. resulted when people in the Stone Age found the need to share complex information.
   d. was made possible by the introduction of the steam engine.

_____ 16. The telephone and radio were developed in the _____ Age.
   a. Agricultural Age
   b. Industrial Age
   c. Information Age
   d. Stone Age

_____ 17. Which of the following is not a basic resource needed for technology?
   a. capital   b. time   c. strength   d. information

_____ 18. Communication technologies include
   a. computer numerical control systems.
   b. processes used to move people and goods.
   c. construction of factories to produce goods.
   d. cranes and conveyors.

_____ 19. One of the goals of bio-related technologies is to
   a. create tools to help manufacture products at a lower cost.
   b. help move people and products efficiently.
   c. help preserve the environment.
   d. make sure that product designs meet human needs.

_____ 20. A command given to a computer system is an example of
   a. a process.   b. an input.   c. an output.   d. feedback.

Chapter Review **2**

Design and Problem Solving

I. Vocabulary Review

Unscramble each of the following terms and write it on the line to the left of the correct definition.

neontivio ceogrimson stingchek grinnabriostr prepanacea
gisden niniotavon trotepopy sefribendig nidregren

_____ 1. The process of designing new products

_____ 2. Matching design with human needs

_____ 3. Preliminary type of two-dimensional model

_____ 4. Group problem solving in which people suggest ideas

_____ 5. Model that resembles a finished product, but does not work

_____ 6. Plan for making something

_____ 7. Introduction of something new

_____ 8. Working model

_____ 9. Statement of the problem to be solved

_____ 10. Two-dimensional model that prepares the designer for three-dimensional models

II. Concept/Skills Review

In the blank at the left, write the letter of the choice that best completes the statement or answers the question.

_____ 11. After a need has been established, what is the next step in the design process?
a. The solution should be evaluated.
b. The designer should decide on a solution.
c. More information should be gathered about the need.
d. A solution should be implemented.

_____ 12. Which of the following is considered a three-dimensional modeling technique?
a. sketching   b. drawing   c. rendering   d. scale modeling

(continued next page)

_____ 13. Which of the following is *not* part of choosing the best solution for a design problem?
   a. narrowing the list of possibilities
   b. reviewing the advantages and disadvantages of each idea
   c. sketching potential design ideas
   d. looking at all possible solutions

_____ 14. Which of the following is *not* a useful modeling technique?
   a. computer simulations
   b. brainstorming
   c. prototyping
   d. computer-aided design

_____ 15. Which of the following is an example of ergonomics?
   a. developing "user friendly" software
   b. developing a faster computer
   c. preparing a pleasing design for an office
   d. testing products to ensure that they meet their advertised standards

_____ 16. The primary purpose of evaluating the solution to a design problem is to
   a. determine whether to hire the same designer for future projects.
   b. ensure that it meets Underwriters Laboratories standards.
   c. eliminate alternative solutions to the problem.
   d. determine whether it is working properly.

_____ 17. Improvements on the basic light bulb are an example of a(n)
   a. system.   b. innovation.   c. process.   d. prototype.

_____ 18. A student determines that a group of elderly people would benefit from a device to help them reach items in kitchen cabinets. This is an example of
   a. identifying a need.
   b. choosing the best solution.
   c. creating a design brief.
   d. implementing a solution.

_____ 19. One reason that the process of designing is complicated is that
   a. it uses complex mathematical formulas.
   b. much information must be considered.
   c. the process is difficult to implement.
   d. it requires an advanced degree in design.

_____ 20. Talking to people, visiting a museum, and using the Internet are methods of
   a. brainstorming.
   b. modeling possible design solutions.
   c. gathering information.
   d. creating a prototype.

Chapter Review   3

Computer-Aided Drafting (CAD)

I. Vocabulary Review

In the blank at the left, write the word or words that complete each clue. Then find the words in the puzzle on the next page. Note: The puzzle ignores hyphens and spaces. For example, suppose one of the terms is "floppy disk." In the puzzle, you will find this term spelled "FLOPPYDISK," with no space between the words.

Clues:

_____ 1. Designers often create _____, or models of a new design, to help people "see" the new product.

_____ 2. Most CAD systems are based on the _____ coordinate system.

_____ 3. The process of representing three-dimensional objects in two dimensions is known as _____.

_____ 4. The _____, or central processing unit, is the part of a computer that does or directs all of the work the computer does.

_____ 5. A pointing device that is similar to a mouse but is more accurate and flexible is a _____.

_____ 6. The permanent memory in a computer is known as ROM, or _____ memory. (hyphenated word)

_____ 7. In a CAD program, a symbol or part that is used many times can be placed into the drawing instantly by recalling the part from a symbol _____.

_____ 8. A disc that is similar to audio CDs but that can hold text and graphics as well as audio is known as a _____.

_____ 9. CAD is often used with manufacturing tools; this combination is commonly known as CAD/_____.

(continued next page)

Chapter 3 Review (continued)

_____ 10. An input device that is often used to enter existing draw-ings into a CAD system is the _____.

_____ 11. A CAD structure that has three dimensions and can be used to test the weight and strength of an item before it is actually built is a _____. (two words)

```
O  Y  C  R  I  W  E  R  C  N  B  E
C  P  R  O  T  O  T  Y  P  E  S  U
F  A  D  S  E  V  M  P  U  C  K  R
A  D  R  I  O  J  E  S  S  A  D  T
X  I  A  T  V  F  Q  B  L  T  W  I
S  U  F  R  E  A  D  O  N  L  Y  Z
E  D  T  C  S  S  E  C  T  I  B  N
M  W  I  F  O  H  I  C  D  B  T  Y
E  S  N  G  L  I  T  A  V  R  C  K
Q  U  G  L  I  X  S  M  N  A  O  J
T  O  T  M  D  T  C  D  E  R  Y  M
T  H  I  D  M  O  I  W  R  Y  E  N
A  C  F  L  O  C  U  Z  T  R  I  L
W  A  O  K  D  E  A  G  E  M  J  E
D  O  R  H  E  X  O  O  S  R  E  T
A  R  D  I  L  E  W  U  R  H  T  O
```

II. Concept/Skills Review

In the blank at the left, write the letter of the choice that best completes the statement or answers the question.

_____ 12. To locate a specific point on a coordinate system, you must specify two num-bers called a coordinate
a. determiner.
b. combo.
c. locator.
d. pair.

(continued next page)

Chapter 3 Review (continued)

_____ 13. An X coordinate of 5 and a Y coordinate of 3 specifies a point
a. 5 units to the right of the origin and 3 units above the origin.
b. 5 units to the left of the origin and 3 units above the origin.
c. 5 units to the right of the origin and 3 units below the origin.
d. 5 units to the left of the origin and 3 units below the origin.

_____ 14. The Z axis on a coordinate system specifies the _____ of an object.
a. width
b. depth
c. height
d. length

_____ 15. An example of an editing command in a CAD program is
a. MOVE.
b. CIRCLE.
c. TEXT.
d. DIMENSIONING.

_____ 16. An example of a utility command in a CAD program is
a. ARC.
b. LINE.
c. MOVE.
d. PAN.

_____ 17. The difference between the COPY and MIRROR commands on most CAD systems is that the
a. MIRROR command rotates the copy of the object.
b. MIRROR command creates an exact copy of the object.
c. COPY command creates an exact copy of the object.
d. COPY command creates a mirror image of the object.

_____ 18. Because CAD software usually takes up so much room, many CAD programs now come on
a. floppy disks.
b. CD-ROMs.
c. tape cartridges.
d. hard disk drives.

(continued next page)

_____ 19. Using a CAD program does *not* ensure that
    a. a drawing can be changed without redrawing it.
    b. the design you create will be a good design.
    c. many copies of the drawing can be made electronically (without redrawing it).
    d. the drawing can be stored electronically.

_____ 20. A difference between RAM and ROM is that
    a. ROM is permanent memory, and RAM is temporary memory.
    b. ROM is working memory, and RAM is permanent memory.
    c. ROM is working memory, and RAM stores the operating system.
    d. RAM can store information even after a computer has been turned off.

Chapter Review

4

Desktop Publishing

I. Vocabulary Review

Complete the crossword puzzle using the clues provided below.

CLUES:

DOWN

1. producing documents using a computer and special software
2. a type of camera that stores images in a form that computers can read
6. another term for "page number"
7. another term for "drawing"

ACROSS

3. the spacing between lines
4. twelve points in publishing measurement systems
5. remove unwanted portions of a photograph
8. the process of putting writing into printed form
9. device that can change an image into an electronic form usable by computers
10. type of software that combines text and graphics in a document

II. Concept/Skills Review

In the blank at the left, write the letter of the choice that best completes the statement or answers the question.

_____ 11. The number of dots per inch of ink on a printed page determines the _____ of a document.
     a. number of colors   c. resolution
     b. layout   d. type size

_____ 12. The three main categories of typefaces are
     a. large, medium, and small.   c. corporate, sans serif, and individual.
     b. serif, sans serif, and decorative.   d. digital, analog, and encoded.

(continued next page)

_____ 13. Among other things, most basic desktop publishing software allows you to
    a. place text in columns and add photographs.
    b. create complex illustrations.
    c. insert information into a database.
    d. edit images you have imported from other software programs.

_____ 14. Programs that are often used with desktop publishing programs include
    a. image editing programs, drawing programs, and clip art.
    b. drawing programs, word processors, and financial programs.
    c. image editing programs, scheduling software, and financial programs.
    d. drawing programs, disk utilities, and image editing programs.

_____ 15. Existing photographs can be changed to an electronic form and entered into a document using a(n)
    a. digital camera.   c. inkjet printer.
    b. drafting machine.   d. scanner.

_____ 16. In most publishing measurement systems, one inch is equal to _____ points.
    a. 6   c. 72
    b. 12   d. 144

_____ 17. Two methods of printing in color are
    a. spot color and solid color.
    b. solid color and shades of gray (grayscale).
    c. spot color and process color.
    d. solid color and screened color.

_____ 18. What part of a newsletter identifies the publisher?
    a. masthead   c. folio
    b. nameplate   d. headline

_____ 19. General design guidelines suggest that you use a
    a. serif typeface for body text and a decorative typeface for headings.
    b. serif typeface for body text and a sans serif typeface for headings.
    c. sans serif typeface for body text and a corporate typeface for headings.
    d. digital typeface for body text and an analog typeface for headings.

_____ 20. When you consider graphics for a document, you should
    a. use as many graphics as possible to help readers understand the content.
    b. avoid using graphics unless your supervisor specifically tells you to include them.
    c. use the 1-to-5 rule: one page of graphics for every five pages of text.
    d. select graphics carefully so that they enhance the text without overpowering it.

Chapter Review   5

Computer Animation

I. Vocabulary Review

In the blank, write the word or words that best complete each sentence.

_____ 1. The series of rough sketches that show action and dialogue for an animated sequence is called a(n) _____.

_____ 2. A(n) _____ is a clear plastic sheet on which drawings are traced and painted to create a frame.

_____ 3. Three-dimensional puppets are positioned and photographed in _____ animation.

_____ 4. _____ is an effect that occurs when the brain receives images faster than it can process them.

_____ 5. The _____ in a computer animation signal the beginning and ending of an action sequence.

_____ 6. In computer animation, _____ are often changed and combined to create objects and figures.

_____ 7. A simple animation device that consists of several pages with slightly different drawings placed on top of each other and fastened on one edge is known as a(n) _____.

_____ 8. In hand-drawn animation, each drawing makes up one _____ of the film.

_____ 9. _____ specify the number of frames needed for each word of dialogue.

_____ 10. The technique in which the models for an animated film are made of clay is known as _____.

(continued next page)

II. Concept/Skills Review

In the blank at the left, write the letter of the choice that best completes the statement or answers the question.

_____ 11. The people who decide how characters in an animated film will look and act are the
    a. animators.   c. background artists.
    b. layout artists.   d. producers.

_____ 12. The people who actually draw the characters for an animated film are the
    a. animators.   c. background artists.
    b. layout artists.   d. directors.

_____ 13. The people who draw everything that will appear in a scene except the characters are the
    a. animators.   c. background artists.
    b. layout artists.   d. directors.

_____ 14. A storyboard for an animated film includes
    a. sketches of action only.
    b. the dialogue only.
    c. sketches of action and dialogue.
    d. sketches of action, dialogue, and the number of frames needed for each word of dialogue.

_____ 15. Which of the following is *not* a common use of animation?
    a. commercials   c. action films
    b. textbooks   d. video games

In the blank at the left, write TRUE if the statement is true or FALSE if the statement is false

_____ 16. Cel animation techniques are no longer used in model and computer animation.

_____ 17. The three basic types of animation are hand-drawn, model, and computer animation.

_____ 18. Although the zoetrope was an interesting toy, it had no real effect on the development of animation.

_____ 19. The six steps in producing a three-dimensional computer animation are storyboards, design, layout, cel creation, animation, and photography.

_____ 20. Given the beginning and ending frames, computers are capable of generating the frames in between to simulate motion.

Chapter Review

6

Internet

I. Vocabulary Review

Complete the crossword puzzle using the clues provided below.

CLUES:

DOWN

2. special address system on the World Wide Web: the Uniform ___ Locator
3. the name of the Internet provider
4. text, buttons, or graphics that are attached to links
5. when attached to text or graphics, takes you to other sites or pages
6. messages sent on the Internet
8. changes signals from a computer into signals that can be transmitted over telephone lines

ACROSS

1. software that lets you use the Internet for different kinds of communication
6. the first page of a web site
7. a computer system created by connecting many computers
9. the process of giving or exchanging information

II. Concept/Skills Review

In the blank at the left, write the letter of the choice that best completes the statement or answers the question.

_____ 11. Which of the following statements about the Internet is true?
   a. It was originally set up by computer corporations to provide support to customers.
   b. For security reasons, the Internet is now restricted to use by universities and the military.
   c. It was created in the 1980s.
   d. If one part of it fails, messages are rerouted.

(continued next page)

_____ 12. Which of the following is *not* absolutely necessary to use the Internet?
   a. computer   c. printer
   b. telephone line   d. modem

_____ 13. An Internet service provider (ISP) is a company that
   a. allows people to connect to the Internet.
   b. sells products over the Internet.
   c. repairs Internet computers when they break down.
   d. creates custom web sites for a fee.

_____ 14. The purpose of an acceptable use policy is to
   a. encourage responsible use of the Internet.
   b. keep companies from advertising their products on the Internet.
   c. speed up access time to various Web sites.
   d. provide security for information given out on the Internet.

_____ 15. The three parts of an e-mail address are the
   a. mailbox, company, and domain.   c. user's name, domain, and zone.
   b. mailbox, domain, and zone.   d. user's name, company, and domain.

_____ 16. A URL that ends with ".org" belongs to a(n)
   a. educational organization.   c. nonprofit organization.
   b. commercial firm.   d. network.

_____ 17. TIA is "netspeak" for
   a. thrills in area.   c. try if allowed.
   b. thanks in advance.   d. training in action.

_____ 18. A search engine
   a. searches for keywords at all web sites.
   b. relays a search request to a central Internet search site.
   c. requires a very general search word, such as "pets," to work properly.
   d. checks a catalog of Web sites maintained by a company.

_____ 19. An Internet relay chat
   a. is a real-time system that allows people to talk to each other by typing their messages.
   b. must be restricted to a local area to avoid long-distance telephone charges.
   c. is another term for e-mail.
   d. is a chain of e-mail messages in which each person who receives the e-mail forwards it to someone else in the chat group.

_____ 20. A discussion group for people interested in a particular topic is known as a(n)
   a. chat group.   c. mailing list.
   b. newsgroup.   d. e-mail.

Name _____ Class _____ Date _____

Chapter Review

7

Audio, Video, and Multimedia

I. Vocabulary Review

In the blank, write the word or words that best complete each sentence.

_____ 1. Channels with signals that have a frequency between 54 and 216 megahertz are called _____ channels.

_____ 2. _____ is a combination of several kinds of communication in a single presentation or product.

_____ 3. What we hear on a telecast or broadcast is referred to as _____.

_____ 4. _____ is a type of radio transmission in which the strength of the carrier wave changes.

_____ 5. _____ is a form of energy that is produced by vibrations.

_____ 6. _____ is the part of a telecast that you see.

_____ 7. Channels with signals that have a frequency between 470 and 806 megahertz are called _____ channels.

_____ 8. _____ provides more than one way to get information on a CD-ROM.

_____ 9. A type of radio transmission in which the frequency of the carrier wave changes is _____.

_____ 10. The _____ of a sound wave is the distance between two successive peaks.

II. Concept/Skills Review

In the blank at the left, write the letter of the choice that best completes the statement or answers the question.

_____ 11. The microphone in a radio or television studio
   a. changes sound energy into electrical energy.
   b. changes electrical energy into mechanical energy.
   c. changes mechanical energy into electrical energy.
   d. changes electrical energy into sound energy.

(continued next page)

Chapter 7 Review (continued)

_____ 12. The purpose of a radio transmitter is to
  a. mix live sound with pre-recorded music and commercials.
  b. strengthen the signal for radio reception.
  c. receive sound signals from the radio station.
  d. combine the program signal with the carrier wave.

_____ 13. Which of the following statements is true about radio waves?
  a. FM broadcasts travel a longer distance than AM broadcasts.
  b. AM broadcasts travel a longer distance than FM broadcasts.
  c. AM broadcasts are usually of better quality than FM broadcasts.
  d. AM broadcasts are affected less by static than FM broadcasts.

_____ 14. Which of the following are not considered "talent" in the production of a television program?
  a. reporters
  b. producers
  c. announcers
  d. hosts of game shows

In the blank at the left, write TRUE if the statement is true or FALSE if the statement is false.

_____ 15. Before video information can be used on a CD-ROM, it has to be converted from digital to analog form.

_____ 16. Two types of sensors used in television cameras are the vidicon and the charge-coupled device.

_____ 17. The main parts of a radio are the antenna, tuner, amplifiers, and at least one speaker.

_____ 18. One advantage of digital video is that it is easy to access any part of the video almost immediately.

_____ 19. Multimedia video is of better quality than television because multimedia video uses more frames per second than television.

_____ 20. Over-the-air broadcasting systems provide better reception than satellite systems.

Chapter Review

8

Manufacturing

I. Vocabulary Review

Complete the crossword puzzle using the clues provided below. Note that hyphens, slashes, and spaces between words have been omitted from the puzzle.

CLUES:

DOWN

1. full-size working model
2. changing materials into useful products
3. materials that are used to make products
4. type of production in which products are made to order
5. forming, separating, combining, and conditioning processes

ACROSS

1. mechanical, thermal, and chemical processes
4. mass production system
6. designing and manufacturing a product using computers
7. materials as they occur in nature
8. production system in which a specific quantity of a product is made

II. Concept/Skills Review

In the blanks below, list in order the three basic steps of a manufacturing system.

11. _____

12. _____

13. _____

(continued next page)

Chapter 8 Review (continued)

In the blank at the left, write the letter of the choice that best completes the statement or answers the question.

_____ 14. Materials found in nature are
　　　　a. composite materials.
　　　　b. synthetic materials.
　　　　c. alloys.
　　　　d. natural materials.

_____ 15. Hardwood is wood that comes from trees that
　　　　a. lose their leaves in the fall.
　　　　b. have a dense grain.
　　　　c. keep their leaves all year long.
　　　　d. are more than 10 years old.

_____ 16. Ferrous metals are those that contain
　　　　a. aluminum.　　　　　　c. iron.
　　　　b. copper.　　　　　　　d. zinc.

_____ 17. Which of the following is an example of a composite?
　　　　a. plywood　　　　　　c. plastic
　　　　b. tin　　　　　　　　d. brick

_____ 18. Changing the shape of a material without adding to it or taking anything away is called
　　　　a. separating.
　　　　b. forming.
　　　　c. combining.
　　　　d. conditioning.

_____ 19. The system used to make sure that products meet the standards set by the company, the industry, or the government is
　　　　a. continuous production.
　　　　b. flexible manufacturing.
　　　　c. quality control.
　　　　d. custom production.

_____ 20. Manufacturing systems in which computers control every aspect of manufacturing are known as
　　　　a. CAD/CAM.　　　　　c. CT.
　　　　b. CNC.　　　　　　　d. CIM.

TECHNOLOGY INTERACTIONS Teacher's Resource Guide
Copyright © Glencoe/McGraw-Hill

Name _____ Class _____ Date _____

Chapter Review   9

Structures

I. Vocabulary Review

Listed below are definitions of fluid power terms presented in your text. Print the correct term in the spaces provided beside each definition.

1. _ _ _ _ _ _ _ _ _ _ _ _ _
      1   2

2. _ _ _ _ _ _
      3

3. _ _ _ _ _ _ _ _ _ _ _
         4

4. _ _ _ _ _ _ _ _ _ _ _
    5   6

5. _ _ _ _ _ _ _ _ _
     7   8

6. _ _ _ _ _
       9

7. _ _ _ _ _ _ _ _ _ _ _ _ _
     10   11

8. _ _ _ _
      12

9. _ _ _ _ _ _ _ _ _ _ _ _ _ _ _
       13   14

10. _ _ _ _ _
        15

1. the part of a structure that is above the foundation

2. laws that regulate the kinds of structures that can be built in each part of a community

3. written details about materials and other project-related concerns

4. rules that specify the methods and materials that can be used for each aspect of construction in a city or state

5. the part of a structure that is in contact with the ground

6. a push or pull that transfers energy to an object

7. structures in which lighting, heating, and other systems are controlled by computers

8. an external force on an object

9. building material that can be connected together to make up the frame of a structure

10. drawings that show the builder how to construct a structure

Note that some of the spaces above are numbered. To solve the puzzle below, print the letters in the numbered spaces above in the spaces below that have the same number.

_ , y _ _ _ _ _ _
5 14 4 7 9 14   8 14 15 11 6 3 11 3 6   12   15 2 9 1 13 2 1 9 14   7 1   10 1 15 2

_ .
1 3 8 14 9 15 2 12 3 8   11 2 15   11 3 2 14 3 8 14 8   1 15 14

(continued next page)

Chapter 9 Review (continued)

II. Concept/Skills Review

In the blanks below, list the four parts of a system.

11. _____

12. _____

13. _____

14. _____

In the blank at the left, write the letter of the choice that best completes the statement or answers the question.

_____ 15. A material that is being pushed in opposite directions along adjacent planes is subject to
    a. tension.   c. shear.
    b. compression.   d. torsion.

_____ 16. The two types of load that can be exerted on a structure are
    a. dead loads and static loads.
    b. tension and compression.
    c. live loads and dynamic loads.
    d. static loads and dynamic loads.

_____ 17. Vertical structural supports are known as
    a. columns.   c. trusses.
    b. beams.   d. arches.

_____ 18. What type of plan shows the location of buildings on the lot, as well as sidewalks, driveways, utilities, and streets?
    a. site plan   c. detail drawing
    b. floor plan   d. elevation

_____ 19. The layer of material that is placed between the framing and the finished exterior of a structure is the
    a. partition.   c. substructure.
    b. superstructure.   d. sheathing.

_____ 20. When the owner of a building makes a final inspection, any corrections noted are written on a
    a. specifications list.   c. inspection list.
    b. punch list.   d. formal complaint list.

Chapter Review   10

Flight

I. Vocabulary Review

In the blank at the left, write the word or words that complete each clue. Then find the words in the puzzle on the next page.

Clues:

_____ 1. _____ causes an object to remain still or continue to move in the same direction unless an outside force acts on it.

_____ 2. The cause of resistance an object meets as it moves through the air is _____ friction.

_____ 3. _____ technology is the study of how things fly.

_____ 4. The force that causes moving objects to slow down and stop is _____.

_____ 5. Wing flaps called _____ change the shape of the wing of an aircraft to control lift.

_____ 6. The force of fluid friction on moving objects is _____.

_____ 7. The _____ effect states that a fast-moving fluid exerts less pressure than a slow-moving fluid.

_____ 8. A(n) _____ is a shape designed to speed up air that passes over its top surface.

_____ 9. _____ refers to the force of air on any object that moves through it.

_____ 10. A push or pull that transfers energy to an object is _____.

_____ 11. _____ pulls objects toward the center of the Earth.

(continued next page)

Chapter 10 Review (continued)

```
D A G A E R T A Y M P R O N A L U T
F U R O F D A E R O D Y N A M I C S
A O T E A V I R E R R O P L A Q U I
O O R A I R F O I L X G H I L O P E
K F I C L U N S Z T U D R A G J Y R
T R O W E N A P Y S A E T A R I O M
R I N E R T I A L O F R E Z V W B Q
W C U T O H L C E R F I F S S I J O
P T R A N E B E R N O U L L I L T E
A I E C S I S B L U N O U N T I R Y
E O T R A I B L E G L T I N E C O N
R N G R I V A B T H E Z D O M W H P
```

II. Concept/Skills Review

In the blank at the left, write the letter of the choice that best completes the statement or answers the question.

_____ 12. Two forces that oppose motion are
      a. gravity and friction.
      b. gravity and mass.
      c. friction and mass.
      d. friction and thrust.

_____ 13. Which of the following best describes the effect of drag on an aircraft?
      a. It provides the force needed by an aircraft to overcome friction.
      b. It provides the lift needed by an aircraft to overcome gravity and allow the aircraft to fly.
      c. It is the force of fluid friction on the aircraft and can be reduced by making air flow more smoothly over the surface of an aircraft.
      d. It is equal to the mass of the aircraft multiplied by acceleration of the aircraft due to gravity.

(continued next page)

Chapter 10 Review (continued)

_____ 14. Which part of an airplane is an example of an airfoil?
a. landing gear
b. rudder
c. wings
d. elevators

_____ 15. Newton's third law of motion states that
a. for every action there is an equal and opposite reaction.
b. the change of motion is proportional to the amount of force acting on the body.
c. a fast-moving fluid exerts less pressure than a slow-moving fluid.
d. a body will remain at rest unless a force acts on it.

_____ 16. The forward force that allows planes to fly is
a. lift.
b. friction.
c. thrust,
d. inertia.

_____ 17. A helicopter hovers in one spot when
a. the rotor blades are moved forward.
b. the rotor blades produce only enough lift to match the weight of the helicopter.
c. engine speed matches rotor speed exactly.
d. the rotor blades are moved backward.

_____ 18. Jet engines work on which of the following principles?
a. Einstein's theory of relativity
b. Newton's first law of motion
c. Newton's second law of motion
d. Newton's third law of motion

_____ 19. The propeller on an airplane works by
a. creating low pressure areas in front of the propeller.
b. reducing the air pressure above the wing of the plane.
c. exerting high pressure on the air in front of the airplane.
d. creating thrust.

(continued next page)

Chapter 10 Review (continued)

_____ 20. One of the goals of aerodynamics is to design objects such as airplanes and cars to reduce the effects of
a. fluid friction.
b. thrust.
c. elevation.
d. gravity.

Chapter Review

11

Land and Water Transportation

I. Vocabulary Review

Listed below are definitions of land and water transportation terms presented in your text. Print the correct term in the spaces provided to the left of the definitions.

1. _ _ _ _ _ _ _ _ _ _ _ _ _ _
       1   2   3

2. _ _ _ _ _ _ _
      4   5

3. _ _ _ _ _ _ _ _ _ _ _
    6   7

4. _ _ _ _ _ _
    8   9

5. _ _ _ _ _ _ _ _ _ _ _ _ _ _ _
       10   11   12

   _ _ _ _ _ _

6. _ _ _ _ _ _
     13   14

1. The process by which people, animals, products, and materials are moved from one place to another

2. Upward force a fluid places on an object placed in it

3. Internal-combustion engine that burns fuel by using heat produced by compressing air

4. Type of train that is magnetically lifted and propelled by magnetic fields

5. Engine that creates power by burning fuel inside the engine

6. Water vehicle that transports people and products

Note that some of the spaces above are numbered. To solve the puzzle below, print the letters in the numbered spaces above in the spaces below that have the same number. (Bold means capital letter.)

J _ _ h _ _ _ _ _ _ _ _ _ , _ h _ f _
 10 13   4 1   **13** 14 10 5 4 8   3 9   7 2 13 3 11 9 2 13 10 12 3 10 13 1 7 14

_ _ _ _ _ _ _ _ _ _ _ _ h _ w _ _ _ _ (1895-1898), _ _ _ _ _ _ _ _ _ _ _
1 14 10 12 9   1 2 10 4 12 6   3   9   10 2 14 6   5 10 4 14 6   12 10 3

_ w _ _ .
13 7 8

(continued next page)

II. Concept/Skills Review

In the space beside the number, write the letter of the answer that best completes the statement or answers the question.

_____ 7. A mode is
    a. the process of moving things from place to place.
    b. a method of doing something.
    c. a pathway, or way.
    d. a container.

_____ 8. A transportation system that uses more than one type of transportation is referred to as a(n)
    a. intermodal system.
    b. technological system.
    c. extramodal system.
    d. subsystem.

_____ 9. All types of railroad cars are called
    a. locomotives.
    b. containers.
    c. mass transit.
    d. rolling stock.

_____ 10. A disadvantage of using steam-powered locomotives is that they
    a. are expensive to operate.
    b. release pollutants into the air.
    c. require a great deal of maintenance.
    d. both b and c.

_____ 11. Mass transit refers to
    a. all types of rolling stock.
    b. high-volume freight carriers.
    c. commuter train systems.
    d. long-distance rail passenger service.

_____ 12. Maglev trains are propelled by
    a. magnetically operated wheels.
    b. a guideway.

(continued next page)

Chapter 11 Review (continued)

      c. magnetic fields.

      d. electromagnetic engines.

_____ 13. Most cars use a(n) _____ engine that burns gasoline for power.

      a. gasoline piston

      b. internal-combustion

      c. four-stroke cycle

      d. all of the above

_____ 14. The four strokes in a four-stroke cycle engine and the order in which they are operated are

      a. intake, compression, power, exhaust.

      b. internal, compression, power, exhaust.

      c. intake, conversion, power, exhaust.

      d. intake, compression, piston, exhaust.

_____ 15. One way in which a diesel engine operates differently from a gasoline engine is that

      a. only air is injected into the cylinder during the compression stroke.

      b. it burns diesel fuel as well as gasoline.

      c. hot air ignites the fuel.

      d. the power stroke provides the mechanical energy needed to turn the wheels.

_____ 16. Transportation systems designed to move people and products short distances are called

      a. intermodal transport systems.

      b. people movers.

      c. mass transit systems.

      d. on-site transport systems.

_____ 17. Systems used to transport people, products, and materials across waterways are referred to as

      a. marine transportation.

      b. vessels.

      c. inland water transportation systems.

      d. ferries.

(continued next page)

_____ 18. Boats that require speed usually have
    a. a displacement-style hull.
    b. a planing-style hull.
    c. greater buoyancy.
    d. both a and c.

_____ 19. An object floats in a fluid when
    a. the weight of the object is equal to or greater than the weight of the fluid it displaces.
    b. the upward push on the object is greater than the weight of the fluid.
    c. the weight of the fluid displaced by the object is equal to or greater than the weight of the object.
    d. the buoyant force of the fluid equals the upthrust.

_____ 20. Air-cushion vehicles are also called
    a. hydrofoils.
    b. ground-effect vehicles.
    c. waterjets.
    d. airfoils.

Chapter Review   12

Fluid Power

I. Vocabulary Review

Listed below are definitions of fluid power terms presented in your text. Write the correct term in the space provided beside each definition. Then find and circle the terms in the word search puzzle on the next page. Note that only the first word of one of the multi-word terms appears in the puzzle.

_____ 1. Fluid power systems that use air or another gas

_____ 2. Increase in force gained by using a machine

_____ 3. Any material that flows

_____ 4. Force on a unit surface area

_____ 5. Fluid power systems that use oil or another liquid

_____ 6. The use of pressurized liquids or gases to move heavy objects and perform other tasks

_____ 7. When force is applied to a confined liquid, the resulting pressure is transmitted unchanged to all parts of the liquid.

(continued next page)

```
P N E U M A T I C S Y S T E M S
A R F L S T N I S Y M P S B K M
S R E W O P D I U L F S T N E E
C C U S I E M C A E M R O C R T
A O D F S S P U M P P I H O I S
L N L A U U A S L A S A S M O Y
S T I D C C R A D S N V P P V S
P R P D O T L E I I S A N R R C
R O W E I P U M C R T A R E E I
I L R H I U S A N G E E D S S L
N V Y D C N L I T P N N S S E U
C A R A A P L F E O I U S O R A
I L U R L E M M A L R U R R E R
P V T I C E C T Y I E S C O S D
L E S Y H R E C E I V E R A C Y
E S R O T A L U G E R W O L F H
```

II. Concept/Skills Review

In the space beside the number, write the letter of the answer that best completes the statement.

_____ 8. The three basic systems used to transmit and control power are
a. liquid, gas, and fluid.
b. hydraulic, pneumatic, and fluid.
c. mechanical, electrical, and fluid.
d. solids, liquids, and gases.

_____ 9. All objects are made of
a. solids
b. liquids.
c. gases.
d. matter

_____ 10. The states of matter that have a definite volume are
a. solids and fluids.
b. solids and liquids.
c. solids and gases.
d. solids, liquids, and gases.

(continued next page)

Chapter 12 Review (continued)

_____ 11. An essential factor in all fluid power systems is the
   a. pressure.
   b. compressor
   c. motor.
   d. all of the above.

_____ 12. The component that supplies fluid under pressure to the system is the
   a. control valve.
   b. flow regulator.
   c. compressor or pump.
   d. actuator.

_____ 13. Hydraulic systems include a
   a. compressor and a reservoir.
   b. compressor and a receiver.
   c. pump and a reservoir.
   d. pump and a receiver.

_____ 14. Pneumatic systems include
   a. compressor and a reservoir.
   b. compressor and a receiver.
   c. pump and a reservoir.
   d. pump and a receiver.

_____ 15. The parts that open and close passages to direct the fluid to the proper location in the system are the
   a. flow regulators.
   b. transmission lines.
   c. actuators.
   d. control valves.

_____ 16. Pressure is calculated using the formula
   a. Pressure = Area ÷ Force
   b. Pressure = Force ÷ Area
   c. Pressure = Area × Force
   d. both a and c.

_____ 17. The type of system best suited for tasks requiring strength and accuracy are
   a. hydraulic.
   b. pneumatic.
   c. double-acting.
   d. reciprocating.

(continued next page)

Chapter 12 Review (continued)

_____ 18. A schematic circuit diagram
    a. uses symbols to represent components.
    b. shows how components are arranged.
    c. is read from top to bottom.
    d. all of the above.

_____ 19. In industries, pneumatic devices are used to
    a. perform tasks such as painting.
    b. operate aircraft landing gear.
    c. operate heavy construction equipment.
    d. both a and b.

20. On the lines below, list the components of a fluid power system. Then find and circle the component names in the word search puzzle earlier in this review. Note that only the first word of one of the multi-word names appears in the puzzle. Also, one component name is also a term and should already be marked.

_____

_____

_____

_____

_____

Chapter Review   13

Health Technologies

I. Vocabulary Review

Listed below are definitions of fluid power terms presented in your text. Write the correct term in the spaces of the puzzle whose number is the same as the number of the definition.

CLUES:

DOWN

2. An action that protects the body against a disease.
6. Process of changing the genetic materials that make up living organisms. (___ engineering)

(continued next page)

Chapter 13 Review (continued)

ACROSS

1. Process of examining a patient and studying the symptoms to find out what illness a patient has.
3. The design process that gives special attention to the strengths and limitations of the human body. (___ ___ engineering)
4. The use of engineering principles and design procedures to solve medical problems. (___ engineering)
5. The study of designing equipment and devices that fit the human body, its, movement, and its thinking patterns.
7. A people-made device used to replace a human body part.

II. Concept/Skills Review

In the space beside the number, write the letter of the answer that best completes the statement or answers the question.

_____ 8. The design and construction of physical enhancements is one activity within
   a. genetic engineering.
   b. the diagnostic process.
   c. human factors engineering
   d. ergonomics.

_____ 9. Examples of prostheses include
   a. artificial arms and legs.
   b. false teeth.
   c. replacement heart valves.
   d. all of the above.

_____ 10. Two main types of human technology resources are
   a. prosthetic devices and vaccines.
   b. scientists and engineers.
   c. titanium and plastics.
   d. information and material resources.

_____ 11. The body's natural defense system
   a. is its immune system.
   b. easily accepts artificial materials placed inside the body.
   c. usually rejects artificial joints made of titanium.
   d. both a and c.

(continued next page)

_____ 12. Approximately how many artificial body parts are now made?
   a. 50
   b. 100
   c. 200
   d. 400

_____ 13. Substances placed in the body to increase its immunity to disease are called
   a. remedies.
   b. diagnoses.
   c. vaccines.
   d. injections.

_____ 14. Modern health care technology focuses on three major areas: prevention of disease, treatment, and
   a. diagnosis of illness.
   b. immunization.
   c. monitoring and regulating the body's natural systems.
   d. maintaining a clean, healthy environment in operating rooms.

_____ 15. Two tools that medical technologists use to "see" into the body are the
   a. EKG and EEG.
   b. CAT scan and MRI.
   c. EKG and MRI.
   d. EEG and CAT scan.

_____ 16. Today, ultrasound is used mainly
   a. to prevent disease.
   b. in diagnosis.
   c. in operating rooms.
   d. as a treatment.

_____ 17. Health technologies help us meet many of our physical and psychological needs by providing us with
   a. folk remedies.
   b. immune systems.
   c. enhanced senses and genetic engineering.
   d. products, processes, and procedures.

(continued next page)

_____ 18. When designing equipment and devices, human factors engineers must consider the anatomy of humans as well as their
a. mind and behavior.
b. structural makeup.
c. immune system.
d. genetic materials.

_____ 19. When designing environments, human factors engineers must consider
a. human anatomy and psychology.
b. lighting and temperature.
c. both a and b.
d. both b and c.

_____ 20. The "Americans with Disabilities Act" is a federal law that sets requirements for
a. changing genetic materials to prevent illnesses from occurring.
b. determining which people will receive transplants.
c. designing public places to be accessible to people with disabilities.
d. making public places safe so that disabling accidents do not happen.

Chapter Review   **14**

Environmental Technologies

I. Vocabulary Review

Listed below are definitions of environmental technology terms presented in your text. In the spaces provided below the definitions, print the correct term beside the number that is the same as the number of each definition.

ACROSS

1. A technique used to combine the traits of one animal with those of another animal.
2. Applied science that improves the techniques used to nurture life.
3. The process of growing plants in a soilless environment.
4. The technology of producing the perfect growing conditions so plants can thrive.
5. The study of the passing on of certain traits from parents to offspring.
6. The process plants use to convert sunlight to energy.
7. A tiny particle that carries the genes that pass on inherited characteristics.
8. The introduction of genes from one cell to another cell.
9. The science that studies the laws of heredity.

DOWN

10. A process that uses living microorganisms or parts of organisms to change materials from one form to another.

┌─ 10. (Down)

1. _ _ _ _ _ _ _ _ _ _   _ _ _ _ _ _ _ _
2.   _ _ _ _ _ _ _ _ _ _
    _ _ _ _ _ _ _ _ _ _
3.   _ _ _ _ _ _ _ _ _ _ _
4.   _ _ _ _ _ _ _ _ _ _ _
    _ _ _ _ _ _ _ _ _ _
5.   _ _ _ _ _ _ _ _
6.   _ _ _ _ _ _ _ _ _ _ _ _
7.   _ _ _ _ _ _ _ _ _
8.   _ _ _ _ _ _ _ _
    _ _ _ _ _ _ _ _ _ _ _
9.   _ _ _ _ _ _ _ _

(continued next page)

II. Concept/Skills Review

In the space beside the number, write the letter of the answer that best completes the statement.

_____ 11. Another term for bio-related technologies is
     a. farming.   c. genetic engineering.
     b. environmental technologies.   d. bioprocessing.

_____ 12. The use of machines to make work easier is called
     a. production.   c. mechanization.
     b. bioprocessing.   d. controlled environment agriculture.

_____ 13. The green substance in plants that traps light for photosynthesis is
     a. chlorophyll.   b. carbon dioxide. c. sugar.   d. pollen

_____ 14. In plants, genetic information is passed from one plant to another through
     a. vegetative propagation.   c. bioprocessing.
     b. cross-pollination.   d. hydroponics.

_____ 15. A unit for an inherited trait is a
     a. gene.   b. chromosome.   c. nutrient.   d. cell.

_____ 16. The process of creating plants using cuttings of roots, stems, or leaves is
     a. pollination.   b. hydroponics.   c. CEA.   d. vegetative propagation.

_____ 17. Chemicals that plants need to grow are
     a. nutrients.   b. aggregates.   c. living cells.   d. soil and water.

_____ 18. Aquaculture is
     a. another term for hydroponics.
     b. an aggregate system.
     c. a system in which the exposed roots of plants are misted with nutrients.
     d. the raising of fish and food plants in water.

_____ 19. In bioprocessing, microorganisms are used to
     a. create products such as bread.   c. process waste in treatment plants.
     b. clean polluted bodies of water.   d. all of the above.

20. Answer this question:
    What are the five basic activities involved in growing crops?

_____

_____

_____

_____

Chapter Review **15**

Electricity and Electronics

I. Vocabulary Review

Electricity and electronic terms are defined in the following sentences. However, the letters in the boldfaced words are scrambled. Write the correct spelling of the term on the line beside the number.

_____ 1. A cutriic is the pathway through which electrons travel.

_____ 2. The laonpitte fredefinic is the force that causes electrons to flow.

_____ 3. The movement of electrons from one atom to another is eyecciittrl.

_____ 4. The opposition to the flow of electrons is called cassnterie.

_____ 5. A(n) abertty is a device that converts chemical energy into electrical energy.

_____ 6. The flow of electrons through a conductor is known as turencr.

_____ 7. The rostrainst is a semiconductor device that amplifies and acts as an electronic switch.

_____ 8. A statement of the mathematical relationship between current, voltage, and resistance is Om'sh awl.

_____ 9. A trrongeea is a device that changes mechanical energy into electrical energy.

_____ 10. The relationship between electricity and magnetism is called eraesltmniecogtm.

II. Concept/Skills Review

In the space beside the number, write the letter of the answer that best completes the statement.

_____ 11. An atom consists of a nucleus surrounded by a cloud of
      a. electrons.   b. protons.   c. neutrons.   d. ions.

(continued next page)

Name _____ Class _____ Date _____

_____ 12. The law that states that like-charged particles tend to repel each other and unlike-charged particles attract each other is called
    a. the law of potential.   c. the law of charges.
    b. the ionization law.   d. Ohm's law.

_____ 13. The force that causes electrons to flow is
    a. current.   c. voltage.
    b. electricity.   d. a conductor.

_____ 14. The unit of measure for resistance is the
    a. ion.   c. ohm.
    b. ampere.   d. electromotive force.

_____ 15. When voltage is applied to a conductor, the current that moves through the conductor is directly proportional to the
    a. resistance of the conductor.   c. number of ohms.
    b. applied voltage.   d. size of the circuit.

_____ 16. A simple circuit consists of a power source, a conductor, and
    a. electrodes.   c. resistance.
    b. a current.   d. a load.

_____ 17. The type of circuit in which components are arranged in separate branches is the
    a. series circuit.   c. closed circuit.
    b. open circuit.   d. parallel circuit.

_____ 18. Electronics is the study of
    a. electricity.   c. current.
    b. electrons.   d. voltage levels.

_____ 19. In a combination n-type and p-type semiconductor, electrons flow from the n-type, which has too many electrons, to the p-type, which has too few, through a device known as a junction
    a. diode.   c. emitter.
    b. amplifier.   d. transistor.

_____ 20. When you turn on a transistor radio, the music you hear is the electronic system's
    a. input.   c. process.
    b. control.   d. output.

TECHNOLOGY INTERACTIONS Teacher's Resource Guide
Copyright © Glencoe/McGraw-Hill

Chapter Review   16

Computer Control Systems

I. Vocabulary Review

Listed below are definitions of computer control system terms presented in your text. In the spaces provided below the definitions, print the correct term beside the number that is the same as the number of each definition.

ACROSS

1. Control system that uses computers to operate machines during production
2. Using computers to manufacture a product
3. Software that provides tools for drawing and dimensioning a product
4. Letter-number combinations used in a CNC program that locate points for machine operations in manufacturing a product.
5. Software that can test a product design by simulating the environment in which the product must be able to work.
6. System that allows manufacturers to make many designs using the same machines.

DOWN

7. A combination of computer-aided design and computer-aided manufacturing.

⌐7. (Down)

1. _ _ _ _ _ _ _ _ _ _ _ _ _ _ _ _ _ _ _ _ _ _ _ _ _
2. _ _ _ _ _ _ _ _ _-_ _ _ _ _ _ _ _ _ _ _ _ _ _ _ _ _
3. _ _ _ _ _ _ _ _-_ _ _ _ _ _ _ _ _ _ _ _
4. _ _ _ _ _ _ _ _ _ _ _ _ _ _ _ _ _
5. _ _ _ _ _ _ _ _ _ _ _ _ _ _ _ _ _ _ _
6. _ _ _ _ _ _ _ _ _ _ _ _ _ _ _ _ _ _ _ _ _ _

_ _ _ _ _ _ _

II. Concept/Skills Review

In the space beside each number, write the letter of the answer that best completes the statement or answers the question.

_____ 8. To manufacture a product, detailed and accurate _____ drawings are needed.
   a. sketched   b. 3D   c. working   d. precision

(continued next page)

_____ 9. When using CAD, which of the following devices is *not* used to input information into the computer?
a. mouse   b. keyboard   c. plotter   d. digitizer

_____ 10. Images created using CAD can be saved
a. on the computer's hard drive.   c. in a library of symbols.
b. on a floppy disk.   d. all of the above.

_____ 11. Simulation software is used
a. to test product designs.   c. to make calculations.
b. instead of prototypes.   d. all of the above.

_____ 12. The type of software that can "bring an object to life" on the computer screen is _____ software.
a. 3D drawing   b. animation   c. automation   d. digital analysis

_____ 13. Using a machine to remove material from stock until a part is shaped is called
a. machining.   b. carving.   c. spinning.   d. rounding.

_____ 14. The two most common machine tools are the
a. milling machine and end mill.   c. spindle and lathe.
b. end mill and spindle.   d. lathe and milling machine.

_____ 15. In a numerical control system, instructions are input into machines using
a. computers.   b. floppy disks.   c. MDI.   d. all of the above.

_____ 16. When manufacturing a part on a CNC machine, the person who selects the stock, loads the program, and operates the machine is the
a. programmer.   b. drafter.   c. machinist.   d. engineer.

_____ 17. Instructions are input into CNC machines in the form of
a. codes.   b. data.   c. coordinates.   d. axes.

_____ 18. Numerical control is a type of
a. CAD.   b. CAM.   c. MDI.   d. FMS.

_____ 19. Using a CAD/CAM system in manufacturing
a. saves time.   c. increases the need for programs.
b. increases accuracy.   d. both a and b.

_____ 20. In just-in-time manufacturing,
a. workstations are called cells.
b. parts are delivered just before they are needed.
c. warehouses are used extensively.
d. all of the above.

Chapter Review 17

Robotics

I. Vocabulary Review

Listed below are definitions of robotic terms presented in your text. Write the correct term in the space provided beside each definition.

_____ 1. A machine made to act like a living thing

_____ 2. Technique used to make a process automatic

_____ 3. Ability of a robot to move in a specific direction

_____ 4. The study of robotics

_____ 5. Process of sending signals, interpreting received signals, and adjusting through signals

_____ 6. Space within which a robotic arm moves

II. Concept/Skills Review

Write the words that correctly complete the following statements on the lines beside the numbers of the statements.

_____ 7. Robotics is a _____ _____ technology.

_____ 8. When Herman Hollerith invented the punch card tabulating machine in the late 1800s, he created an electrical _____ and _____, important technology in the development of robots.

_____ 9. Robotic arms are also called _____.

_____ 10. When robotic arms must lift heavy loads, _____ and _____ power systems are often used.

_____ 11. Teaching a robot by guiding it through a sequence of movements is called _____-_____ _____.

_____ 12. The use of robots in business and industry is part of the _____ revolution.

(continued next page)

Chapter 17 Review (continued)

In the space beside the number, write the letter of the answer that best completes the statement.

_____ 13. Modern robots can be used in
   a. certain surgical procedures.   c. police work.
   b. underwater explorations.   d. all of the above.

_____ 14. The development in the 1940s that reduced the size of computers and increased their speed was the
   a. transistor.   c. electrical sensor.
   b. nonomachine.   d. numerical control system.

_____ 15. Robotic hands are called
   a. manipulators.   c. actuators.
   b. end effectors.   d. joints.

_____ 16. Places where two moving parts of a robot are connected are called
   a. manipulators.   c. actuators.
   b. end effectors.   d. joints.

_____ 17. The power source commonly used to operate robotic arms is a
   a. computer.   c. stepper motor.
   b. manipulator.   d. robotic interface.

_____ 18. The series of instructions computers use to control the movement of a robotic arm is called
   a. a program.   c. binary code.
   b. a flowchart.   d. feedback.

_____ 19. While they work, robots feed information back to the computer through
   a. actuators.   c. nerve bundles.
   b. sensors.   d. both a and b.

_____ 20. Today's robots
   a. are second-generation robots.
   b. can be taught to do several operations.
   c. are extremely accurate.
   d. all of the above.

Chapter Review

18

Lasers and Fiber Optics

I. Vocabulary Review

Listed below are definitions of fluid power terms presented in your text. Write the correct term in the spaces of the puzzle whose number is the same as the number of the definition.

DOWN

1. Light that spreads out very little compared to ordinary light (two words)
2. Wave produced by the motion of electrically charged particles (two words)
3. Light that consists of one color (two words)
6. Light in which all of the light waves have the same wavelength (two words)

ACROSS

4. A tiny unit of light energy
5. Photographic process that uses a laser, lenses, and mirrors to produce three-dimensional images.
7. Light source that sends out light in a narrow, strong beam

II. Concept/Skills Review

In the space beside the number, write the letter of the answer that best completes the statement or answers the question.

_____ 8. Light travels in
    a. filaments.
    b. charged particles.
    c. waves.
    d. electricity.

(continued next page)

Chapter 18 Review (continued)

_____ 9. Forms of electromagnetic radiation include
    a. visible light.   c. X rays.
    b. radio waves.   d. all of the above.

_____ 10. Ordinary light is a type of
    a. electromagnetic wave.   c. directional light.
    b. monochromatic light.   d. coherent light.

_____ 11. Laser light
    a. is a mixture of many colors.   c. is brighter than ordinary light.
    b. is not usually visible.   d. does not travel in waves.

_____ 12. Lasers are grouped into four classes according to
    a. their energy source.   b. the hazard they present.
    c. their active medium.   d. the tasks they perform.

_____ 13. Which of the following is *not* a basic subsystem of the laser?
    a. an excitation mechanism   c. an active medium
    b. a scanning mechanism   d. a feedback mechanism

_____ 14. The part of the laser system that changes energy to light is the
    a. an excitation mechanism.   c. an active medium.
    b. a scanning mechanism.   d. a feedback mechanism.

_____ 15. The output coupler in a laser system is part of the
    a. an excitation mechanism.   c. an active medium.
    b. a scanning mechanism.   d. a feedback mechanism.

_____ 16. The type of laser used most often in technology classes is the
    a. semiconductor laser.   c. ruby laser.
    b. helium-neon laser.   d. carbon dioxide laser.

_____ 17. Fiber-optic systems send information as
    a. coded light pulses.   c. electronic signals.
    b. continuous beams.   d. all of the above.

_____ 18. In a fiber-optic telephone system, sound travels in
    a. watts.   b. audio waves.   c. bits.   d. electronic signals.

_____ 19. In manufacturing, lasers are used to
    a. drill holes in materials.   c. weld parts on ships.
    b. cut heavy steel plates.   d. all of the above.

_____ 20. Which of the following is *not* a characteristic of laser light?
    a. travels in waves   c. narrow, strong beam
    b. mixture of many colors   d. directional

TECHNOLOGY INTERACTIONS Teacher's Resource Guide
Copyright © Glencoe/McGraw-Hill

Chapter Review   19

Engineering

I. Vocabulary Review

Following is a list of definitions of key terms in this chapter. Write the term being defined in the space provided beside the number of each definition.

_____ 1. A process used to develop solutions to problems

_____ 2. A problem-solving process and a design process

_____ 3. Rules or models against which a product, action, or process can be compared

_____ 4. A person who uses his or her knowledge of science, technology, and mathematics to solve technical problems.

II. Concept/Skills Review

In the space beside the number, write the letter of the answer that best completes the statement or answers the question.

_____ 5. Solutions to engineering problems may be in the form of
    a. products.   c. designs.
    b. methods.   d. all of the above.

_____ 6. Which of the following is not considered a "classic" type of engineering?
    a. manufacturing engineering   c. civil engineering
    b. mechanical engineering   d. electronics engineering

_____ 7. Public works engineering is done by
    a. mechanical engineers.   c. infrastructure engineers.
    b. civil engineers.   d. mining engineers.

_____ 8. Machines and machine parts are designed by
    a. manufacturing engineers.   c. mechanical engineers.
    b. systems engineers.   d. machinists.

_____ 9. The development of robots in factories is done mainly by
    a. manufacturing engineers.   c. electrical engineers.
    b. manufacturing engineers.   d. design specialists.

(continued next page)

_____ 10. Some _____ engineers specialize in processing metals or refining petroleum.
a. chemical   b. mining   c. manufacturing   d. environmental

_____ 11. Engineers who design circuits and work to develop more efficient motors and lighting are _____ engineers.
a. civil   b. electrical   c. mechanical   d. environmental

_____ 12. The relationship between the number of hours worked and the quantity of products made is called
a. manufacturing engineering.   c. production.
b. production engineering.   d. productivity.

_____ 13. Which of the following is *not* considered a "new-generation" type of engineering?
a. aerospace engineering   c. environmental engineering
b. electronics engineering   d. materials engineering

_____ 14. Engineers who design cleaner production methods to meet government regulations are
a. manufacturing engineers.   c. environmental engineers.
b. chemical engineers.   d. industrial designers.

_____ 15. A spin-off of electronics engineering is
a. computer engineering.   c. aerospace engineering.
b. electrical engineering.   d. both a and c.

_____ 16. People who specialize in improving product designs that already exist are
a. mechanical engineers.   c. industrial designers.
b. manufacturing engineers.   d. "new generation" engineers.

_____ 17. The first step in the engineering process is to
a. gather information.   c. identify the need.
b. develop alternative solutions.   d. evaluate the solution.

_____ 18. Brainstorming is a part of which step in the engineering process?
a. developing alternative solutions   c. categorizing the problem
b. gathering information   d. implementing the solution

_____ 19. Models are made to
a. test solution ideas.   c. develop alternative solutions.
b. communicate design ideas.   d. both a and b.

_____ 20. The final test before manufacturing takes place is
a. building a working model.   c. matching the design criteria.
b. checking the design checklist.   d. building a prototype.

Chapter Review

20

Applied Physics

I. Vocabulary Review

Listed below are definitions of applied physics terms presented in your text. Print the correct term in the spaces provided beside the definitions.

1. $\underset{1}{\rule{0.3cm}{0.4pt}}$ $\rule{0.3cm}{0.4pt}$ $\rule{0.3cm}{0.4pt}$ $\rule{0.3cm}{0.4pt}$ $\underset{2}{\rule{0.3cm}{0.4pt}}$ $\rule{0.3cm}{0.4pt}$ $\rule{0.3cm}{0.4pt}$ $\underset{3}{\rule{0.3cm}{0.4pt}}$ $\rule{0.3cm}{0.4pt}$ $\rule{0.3cm}{0.4pt}$

2. $\rule{0.3cm}{0.4pt}$ $\rule{0.3cm}{0.4pt}$ $\underset{4}{\rule{0.3cm}{0.4pt}}$ $\rule{0.3cm}{0.4pt}$ $\underset{5}{\rule{0.3cm}{0.4pt}}$

3. $\underset{6}{\rule{0.3cm}{0.4pt}}$ $\rule{0.3cm}{0.4pt}$ $\rule{0.3cm}{0.4pt}$ $\rule{0.3cm}{0.4pt}$ $\underset{7}{\rule{0.3cm}{0.4pt}}$ $\rule{0.3cm}{0.4pt}$

4. $\underset{8}{\rule{0.3cm}{0.4pt}}$ $\rule{0.3cm}{0.4pt}$ $\rule{0.3cm}{0.4pt}$ $\rule{0.3cm}{0.4pt}$ $\underset{9}{\rule{0.3cm}{0.4pt}}$

5. $\underset{10}{\rule{0.3cm}{0.4pt}}$ $\underset{11}{\rule{0.3cm}{0.4pt}}$ $\rule{0.3cm}{0.4pt}$ $\rule{0.3cm}{0.4pt}$ $\rule{0.3cm}{0.4pt}$ $\rule{0.3cm}{0.4pt}$

6. $\rule{0.3cm}{0.4pt}$ $\rule{0.3cm}{0.4pt}$ $\underset{12}{\rule{0.3cm}{0.4pt}}$ $\rule{0.3cm}{0.4pt}$ $\rule{0.3cm}{0.4pt}$ $\rule{0.3cm}{0.4pt}$ $\underset{13}{\rule{0.3cm}{0.4pt}}$
$\rule{0.3cm}{0.4pt}$ $\rule{0.3cm}{0.4pt}$ $\underset{14}{\rule{0.3cm}{0.4pt}}$ $\rule{0.3cm}{0.4pt}$ $\rule{0.3cm}{0.4pt}$ $\rule{0.3cm}{0.4pt}$

7. $\rule{0.3cm}{0.4pt}$ $\underset{15}{\rule{0.3cm}{0.4pt}}$ $\underset{16}{\rule{0.3cm}{0.4pt}}$ $\rule{0.3cm}{0.4pt}$

8. $\rule{0.3cm}{0.4pt}$ $\rule{0.3cm}{0.4pt}$ $\underset{17}{\rule{0.3cm}{0.4pt}}$$\underset{18}{\rule{0.3cm}{0.4pt}}$

9. $\rule{0.3cm}{0.4pt}$ $\rule{0.3cm}{0.4pt}$ $\rule{0.3cm}{0.4pt}$ $\underset{19}{\rule{0.3cm}{0.4pt}}$ $\underset{20}{\rule{0.3cm}{0.4pt}}$

1. The study of the ways in which objects are moved and work is done

2. The application of force to cause an object to move in the direction of the force

3. A device designed to obtain the greatest amount of force from the energy used

4. The force of attraction that exists between two objects

5. A force that opposes motion

6. The number of times a machine multiplies a force

7. A push or pull applied to an object

8. The rate at which work is done or how much work is accomplished in a certain period of time

9. The tendency of an object to continue to move or to stay at rest

(continued next page)

Chapter 20 Review (continued)

Note that some of the spaces above are numbered. To solve the puzzle below, print the letters in the numbered spaces above in the spaces below that have the same number. (Bold means capital letter.)

J __ __ __ __ __ __ __ __ __ __ __ __ x __ __ __ __ (1831-1879), __ b __ __ __ __ __ __ __ __
  20 6 17 3   **16** 13 17 18 5   **6** 20   4 17 11 11   20   18 11 13 13 11 20 7 19

__ __ __ __ __ __ __ __ __ __ , __ __ __ __ __ __ b __ __ __ __ __ __ __ __ __ __ __ __ __ __ __ __ __
1 12 9 3 11 16 11 3 19   2 17 3 16 18 11   17 2   17 13 17 16 19 18 15 6 20 8 7 17 19 11 16

__ __ __ __ __ 20 __ __ __ __ __ b __ __ __ __ __ __ __ __ __ __ __ __ u __ __ __ __
4 20 14 17 3   9 17 20 18 3   17 10 15 18 17   20 7 9 15 7 17   20 16 19   20 13 13 9

__ b __ __ __ __ __ __ __ __ __ __ . __ x __ __ __ __ __ __ __ __ __ __ __ __ __ __ u __
15   3 17 18 14 17 2   19 12 17 6   **6** 20   4 17 13 13   15 10 19 17 7   4 15 18 5 17 2   15   19

__ __ __ __ __ __ __ b __ __ __ __ __ __ __ __ __ __ __ __ __ __
12 11 3   11 2 17 20 3   9   12 20 14 11 7 8   11 6 20 8 11 7 20 18 9

__ , __ __ b __ .
16 15 7 14 17 18 3 20 19 11 15 7 3   4 11 19 12   12 11 3   2 15 18   **19** 15   11

II. Concept/Skills Review

In the space beside each number, write the letter of the answer that best completes the statement or answers the question.

_____ 10. Motion involves
     a. force.
     b. friction.
     c. gravity.
     d. all of the above.

_____ 11. The force that acts in the direction opposite the direction of the motion is
     a. gravity.
     b. friction.
     c. energy.
     d. pressure.

_____ 12. The minimum speed at which an object must travel to escape Earth's gravitational pull is
     a. equal to or greater than the object's weight.
     b. the escape velocity.
     c. 40,000 km/h.
     d. both b and c.

(continued next page)

Chapter 20 Review (continued)

_____ 13. Dynamics is the study of the movement of an object and
    a. drag.
    b. its shape.
    c. the forces acting on it.
    d. its inertia.

_____ 14. Which of the following is *not* one of Newton's laws of motion?
    a. For every action, there is an equal and opposite reaction.
    b. Objects move only when a force is applied to them.
    c. An object at rest will stay at rest, and an object in motion will stay in motion.
    d. The rate at which an object moves depends on the size of the unbalanced force acting on it and the mass of the object.

_____ 15. To calculate work, multiply the force by the
    a. distance.
    b. time.
    c. weight.
    d. mass.

_____ 16. Sound travels most easily through
    a. solid material.
    b. liquids.
    c. a vacuum.
    d. gases.

_____ 17. Sound that is so high-pitched that we cannot hear it is
    a. a sound wave.
    b. sound energy.
    c. sonar.
    d. ultrasound.

_____ 18. The source of all light energy is
    a. electricity.
    b. the atom.
    c. photons.
    d. electromagnetic waves.

(continued next page)

Chapter 20 Review (continued)

_____ 19. The four important properties of light are speed, amplitude, frequency, and
   a. electromagnetism.
   b. pattern.
   c. wavelength.
   d. visibility.

_____ 20. A narrow, high-energy beam of parallel light rays is
   a. incandescent.
   b. a microwave.
   c. a laser beam.
   d. visible light.

TECHNOLOGY INTERACTIONS Teacher's Resource Guide
Copyright © Glencoe/McGraw-Hill

Chapter Test 1

How Technology Works

I. Using Vocabulary

Match each item in Column I with the most appropriate item in Column II. Write the letter for that item in the blank at the left.

Column I

_____ 1. science put to practical use

_____ 2. the part of a system in which something is done

_____ 3. all the things needed to produce a product

_____ 4. a form of "commuting" in which people use technology to produce products or services for a company while working in the home

_____ 5. a technology used to control manufacturing processes in factories

_____ 6. something entered into a system

_____ 7. an object used to carry on work

_____ 8. the result of a process

_____ 9. information about the output of a system

_____ 10. an orderly way of achieving a goal

Column II

a. system
b. input
c. process
d. technology
e. computer-integrated manufacturing
f. feedback
g. resources
h. operation
i. output
j. electronic cottage
k. tool

II. Understanding Concepts and Applying Skills

In the blank at the left, write the TRUE if the statement is true or FALSE if the statement is false.

_____ 11. People in prehistoric times used the stone ax to satisfy their need for food and protection, as well as to construct basic dwellings and other necessities.

_____ 12. To be usable, most raw materials must be processed.

(continued next page)

_____ 13. The Industrial Age came about as a direct result of the Information Age.

_____ 14. The activities of technology that are used to produce products include manufacturing, construction, transportation, communication, and bio-related technologies.

_____ 15. Although all technology uses a system of some type, the systems may operate in very different ways.

Answer the following questions in phrases or complete sentences.

16. What need leads to the development of most tools?

_____

_____

17. What causes people to have such different ways of life from one era to another? Explain.

_____

_____

18. In what ways have the electronics produced during the Information Age affected all technologies? Explain.

_____

_____

19. Explain the statement, "It takes many of the same types of resources to produce a stone ax as it does to write a computer program."

_____

_____

_____

20. Using an example of your choice, explain how each part of a typical system works.

_____

_____

_____

Name _____ Class _____ Date _____

Chapter Test   2

Design and Problem Solving

I. Using Vocabulary

Match each item in Column I with the most appropriate item in Column II. Write the letter for that item in the blank at the left.

Column I

_____ 1. group technique of suggesting ideas as they occur

_____ 2. detailed, two-dimensional model often created with colored pencils and markers

_____ 3. introduction of something

_____ 4. a plan that is used to make something

_____ 5. matching design to human needs

_____ 6. type of three-dimensional model that is small, but accurate

_____ 7. rough, two-dimensional model that helps people put their ideas on paper

_____ 8. a working model

_____ 9. model that looks like a finished product but does not work

_____ 10. the process of designing new products

Column II

a. innovation
b. brainstorming
c. sketch
d. ergonomic
e. invention
f. technology
g. appearance model
h. rendering
i. scale model
j. prototype
k. design

II. Understanding Concepts and Applying Skills

In the blank at the left, write the TRUE if the statement is true or FALSE if the statement is false.

_____ 11. When a problem must be solved quickly, good designers save time by not developing alternative solutions.

_____ 12. Experienced problem solvers sometimes use the steps of the design process in slightly different ways to achieve a solution.

(continued next page)

_____ 13. A clear statement of the problem is essential to designing a solution.

_____ 14. Brainstorming is a group problem solving technique.

_____ 15. The difference between invention and innovation is that innovation produces entirely new products, but invention improves products that already exist.

Answer the following questions in phrases or complete sentences.

16. Explain the six steps of the design process.

_____

_____

_____

17. Explain the relationship between the design process and making decisions.

_____

_____

18. What part does the design process play in design?

_____

_____

19. You have identified a need for a new design that makes it easier for very young children to grasp a spoon and eat their food with minimal adult help. You have followed the design process and invented a spoon to meet this need. How will you evaluate your solution to this design problem?

_____

_____

20. Three-dimensional models such as prototypes offer much information that is not available from two-dimensional models. Explain why both types of models are often used in the development of a new product.

_____

_____

_____

Chapter Test   3

Computer-Aided Drafting (CAD)

I. Using Vocabulary

Match each item in Column I with the most appropriate item in Column II. Write the letter for that item in the blank at the left.

Column I	Column II
_____ 1. permanent memory in a computer	a. CAD
_____ 2. vertical axis on a coordinate system	b. RAM
_____ 3. coordinate system used in CAD	c. solid model
_____ 4. using a computer to create drafted documents	d. Cartesian
_____ 5. axis used for depth in a three-dimensional drawing	e. ROM
	f. X
_____ 6. working memory in a computer	g. Y
_____ 7. three-dimensional drawing that shows solid sides but does not have weight or strength characteristics	h. CPU
	i. surface model
_____ 8. small-scale model of a new design	j. Z
	k. wireframe
_____ 9. see-through drawing, similar to a stick drawing, that shows the length, width, and height of an object	l. prototype
_____ 10. three-dimensional drawing that can be used to test the strength of a newly designed object	

(continued next page)

II. Understanding Concepts and Applying Skills

In the blank at the left, write the letter of the choice that best completes the statement or answers the question.

_____ 11. Which of the following coordinate pairs describes a point located 6 units to the right and 2 units above the origin?
   a. (2,6)
   b. (–2,6)
   c. (6,–2)
   d. (6,2)

_____ 12. A line whose endpoints are at (3,3) and (3,9) is
   a. at a 45° angle.
   b. horizontal.
   c. vertical.
   d. at a 30° angle.

_____ 13. Which two basic CAD commands should you use to make a copy of an object at a 25° angle?
   a. COPY, MIRROR
   b. COPY, ROTATE
   c. MOVE, ROTATE
   d. MOVE, MIRROR

Answer the following questions in phrases or complete sentences.

14. It is possible to use most CAD software with either a mouse or a digitizer and puck. Describe a situation in which you would prefer to use the digitizer and puck. When might you prefer to use a mouse?

_____

_____

_____

_____

(continued next page)

Chapter 3 Test (continued)

15. Explain the advantages of using a CAD system instead of using traditional drafting methods.

_____

_____

_____

_____

16. Why is CAD software not considered a replacement for a skilled drafter?

_____

_____

_____

17. Describe at least five uses of CAD in industry.

_____

_____

_____

_____

_____

_____

18. How is a CAD system different from an ordinary (non-CAD) computer system?

_____

_____

_____

_____

_____

(continued next page)

19. List the coordinates you would enter to create the rectangle. Be sure to use coordinates that place it exactly as shown on the coordinate grid. Begin with the coordinate pair for the lower left corner and continue counterclockwise.

_____

_____

_____

_____

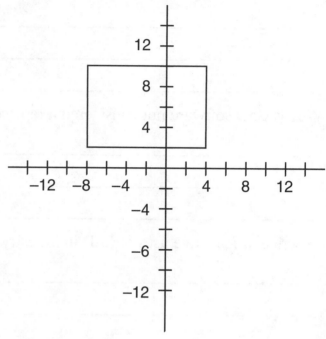

20. Most CAD systems have the ability to zoom in on small parts of a drawing. Why, then, are large monitors usually preferred for CAD work?

_____

_____

_____

_____

Chapter Test

4

Desktop Publishing

I. Using Vocabulary

Match each item in Column I with the most appropriate item in Column II. Write the letter for that item in the blank at the left.

Column I

_____ 1. the process of putting writing into printed form

_____ 2. a device that can change a photograph into an electronic form that a computer can use

_____ 3. the number of dots of ink per inch (dpi) on a printed page

_____ 4. a device that can produce electronic images such as photographs that can be sent directly to a computer

_____ 5. the use of a computer and special software to produce documents

_____ 6. unit of measurement used in publishing; in most systems, 72 of these units equal 1 inch

_____ 7. a set of letters, numbers, and symbols that look the same

_____ 8. the spacing between lines in a document

_____ 9. software that combines text and graphics in a document

_____ 10. unit of measurement used in publishing; six of these units equal 1 inch

Column II

a. publishing
b. image editing program
c. digital camera
d. pica
e. typeface
f. resolution
g. scanner
h. page layout program
i. leading
j. desktop publishing
k. point

(continued next page)

Chapter 4 Test (continued)

II. Understanding Concepts and Applying Skills

Complete each of the following sentences by writing the correct term in the space provided.

_____ 11. The three basic kinds of typefaces are serif, _____, and decorative.

_____ 12. Variations of a typeface such as bold and italic are known as _____.

_____ 13. The two types of graphics used in publications are line art and _____.

_____ 14. The type of color used to reproduce color photographs and art in high-quality publications is _____ color.

_____ 15. The page number that appears on each page of a document is the _____.

Answer the following questions in phrases or complete sentences.

16. Briefly describe the software and hardware needed for desktop publishing.

   _____

   _____

17. What things should you consider when you design a document?

   _____

   _____

18. Explain why it is important to choose the right leading and line length for a document.

   _____

   _____

19. Describe typical uses for each of the three basic kinds of typefaces.

   _____

   _____

20. Explain the difference between a scanner and a digital camera.

   _____

   _____

TECHNOLOGY INTERACTIONS Teacher's Resource Guide
Copyright © Glencoe/McGraw-Hill

Chapter Test   5

Computer Animation

I. Using Vocabulary

Match each item in Column I with the most appropriate item in Column II. Write the letter for that item in the blank at the left.

Column I

_____ 1. effect created when the brain receives images faster than it can process them

_____ 2. the beginning and ending frames in an action sequence

_____ 3. people who draw the characters for a scene

_____ 4. basic geometric shapes that are changed and combined to create complex shapes in computer animation

_____ 5. type of animation in which 3D puppets are used

_____ 6. people who determine how characters will look and act

_____ 7. series of sketches that provide a "blueprint" for making a film

_____ 8. forms that specify the number of frames needed for each word of dialogue

_____ 9. people who draw everything in a scene except the characters

_____ 10. sequence of drawings fastened at one edge that create the illusion of motion when thumbed through rapidly

Column II

a. layout artists
b. primitives
c. exposure sheets
d. persistence of vision
e. key frames
f. background artists
g. flip-book
h. cel animation
i. model
j. storyboards
k. animators

(continued next page)

II. Understanding Concepts and Applying Skills

Name and briefly describe the three types of modern animation techniques.

11. _____

12. _____

13. _____

Answer the following questions in phrases or complete sentences.

14. Explain the difference between a storyboard and an exposure sheet.

_____

_____

15. What is the purpose of the shading step in 3D computer animation?

_____

16. Explain the relationship among shading, lighting, and rendering in the computer animation process.

_____

_____

17. Explain how the use of key frames in computer animation speeds up the process.

_____

_____

18. Explain how models are created for computer animation.

_____

_____

19. Name three skills that are needed for both traditional and computer animation.

_____

_____

20. List at least three current uses for animation.

_____

_____

Chapter Test   6

Internet

I. Using Vocabulary

Match each item in Column I with the most appropriate item in Column II. Write the letter for that item in the blank at the left.

Column I

_____ 1. communication system created by connecting many computers

_____ 2. messages sent over the Internet

_____ 3. being polite on the Internet

_____ 4. changes computer signals so they can be transmitted over telephone lines

_____ 5. when attached to text or graphics, can take you to another page or site

_____ 6. address system for the World Wide Web

_____ 7. giving or receiving information

_____ 8. text, button, or graphic that, when clicked, links to another page or site

_____ 9. the part of an e-mail address that is the name of the Internet provider

_____ 10. company that provides Internet access

Column II

a. home page
b. netiquette
c. hyperlinks
d. communication
e. computer network
f. hypertext
g. e-mail
h. modem
i. service provider
j. domain
k. Uniform Resource Locator

II. Understanding Concepts and Applying Skills

Answer the following questions in phrases or complete sentences.

11. What items are needed to access the Internet?

_____

_____

(continued next page)

12. Explain the importance of being safety conscious while you are on the Internet.

_____

_____

13. What is netiquette? Give at least two examples.

_____

_____

14. What is the purpose of a hyperlink? Give an example of a hyperlink you might find at a Web site on space travel.

_____

_____

15. What are the three parts of an e-mail address?

_____

_____

16. List three zones used in the United States and the type of businesses that use each.

_____

_____

17. Explain the idea that the Internet is "an international network of networks."

_____

_____

18. Besides the speed of the modem, what other factor can affect the speed of Internet communication?

_____

19. Why should you be sure that your service provider has a phone number in your area?

_____

20. In your opinion, what effect will increased access to the Internet have on the public library system in the United States? Explain.

_____

_____

Chapter Test   7

Audio, Video, and Multimedia

I. Using Vocabulary

Match each item in Column I with the most appropriate item in Column II. Write the letter for that item in the blank at the left.

Column I

_____ 1. transmission in which the frequency of the carrier wave changes

_____ 2. the part of a broadcast that we see

_____ 3. television channels with frequencies between 470 and 806 megahertz

_____ 4. combines several forms of communication

_____ 5. use of television that allows students in small, rural schools to participate in advanced classes at a school many miles away

_____ 6. transmission in which the strength of the carrier wave changes

_____ 7. used to make CD-ROMs interactive

_____ 8. television channels with frequencies between 54 and 216 megahertz

_____ 9. the part of a broadcast that we hear

_____ 10. a form of energy produced by vibration

Column II

a. video
b. multimedia
c. wavelength
d. UHF
e. VHF
f. amplitude modulation
g. audio
h. sound
i. hypermedia
j. frequency modulation
k. distance learning

II. Understanding Concepts and Applying Skills

Answer the following questions in phrases or complete sentences.

11. In what three ways can television signals be received in homes?

_____

_____

(continued next page)

Chapter 7 Test (continued)

12. Explain what sound is. How do we hear sounds?

_____

_____

13. What is multimedia?

_____

14. Give an example of how multimedia is used today. In what *other* ways do you think multimedia could be used in the future?

_____

_____

15. In what ways are television and radio alike? In what ways are they different?

_____

_____

16. Explain the basic process of electronic communication.

_____

_____

17. List three current uses for television.

_____

18. Briefly explain how a color television camera works.

_____

_____

19. Describe two kinds of hypermedia.

_____

_____

20. Give two reasons why the quality of CD-ROM video is not as good as that of a video-tape. Do you expect this to change? Explain.

_____

_____

Name _____ Class _____ Date _____

Chapter Test

8

Manufacturing

I. Using Vocabulary

Match each item in Column I with the most appropriate item in Column II. Write the letter for that item in the blank at the left.

Column I

_____ 1. type of production in which products are made to order

_____ 2. mechanical, thermal, and chemical processes

_____ 3. materials as they occur in nature

_____ 4. mass production system

_____ 5. production system in which a specific quantity of a product is made

_____ 6. changing materials into useful products

_____ 7. designing and manufacturing a product using computers

_____ 8. materials that are used to make products

_____ 9. full-size working model

_____ 10. forming, separating, combining, conditioning

Column II

a. continuous production
b. CAD/CAM
c. job-lot production
d. prototype
e. quality control
f. secondary processes
g. custom production
h. manufacturing
i. raw materials
j. industrial materials
k. primary processes

II. Understanding Concepts and Applying Skills

Complete each sentence by writing the correct term in the space provided.

_____ 11. When a metal is combined with one or more other metals or nonmetals, the result is a(n) _____.

_____ 12. A _____ plastic can be heated and shaped only once.

_____ 13. Rolling and forging are examples of _____.

(continued next page)

Chapter 8 Test (continued)

_____ 14. _____ is the process of separating a solid material without destroying any of the material.

_____ 15. A process that changes the internal structure of a material is _____ .

Answer the following questions in phrases or complete sentences.

16. What is the difference between natural and synthetic materials?

_____

_____

_____

17. Explain briefly how ceramics are made.

_____

_____

_____

18. What is the relationship between raw materials and industrial materials?

_____

_____

_____

19. Explain the difference between the processes of stamping and extrusion.

_____

_____

_____

20. Name the three basic types of conditioning, and give an example of each.

_____

_____

_____

_____

Chapter Test 9

Structures

I. Using Vocabulary

Match each item in Column I with the most appropriate item in Column II. Write the letter for that item in the blank at the left.

Column I

_____ 1. something that is constructed, or built

_____ 2. materials that have built-in sensors to warn of unsafe conditions

_____ 3. written details about materials and other project-related concerns

_____ 4. an external force on an object

_____ 5. rules that specify the methods and materials that can be used for each aspect of construction in a city or state

_____ 6. drawings that show the builder how to construct a structure

_____ 7. building materials that can be connected to make up the frame of a structure

_____ 8. the part of a structure that is above the foundation

_____ 9. the part of a structure that is in contact with the ground

_____ 10. laws that regulate the kinds of structures that can be built in each part of a community

Column II

a. superstructure
b. structure
c. smart materials
d. building codes
e. zoning laws
f. foundation
g. load
h. compression
i. specifications
j. structural members
k. plans

(continued next page)

II. Understanding Concepts and Applying Skills

In the blank at the left, write the TRUE if the statement is true or FALSE if the statement is false.

_____ 11. A material that is being pulled by an internal force is being subjected to shear.

_____ 12. Columns must have high compression strength to support the weight of a structure.

_____ 13. A separate site plan is made for each floor of a building to show the arrangements of rooms as viewed from above.

_____ 14. The difference between elevations and section drawings is that elevations show the outside of the structure, and section drawings show the inside.

_____ 15. The walls that support a structure are called *partitions*.

Answer the following questions in phrases or complete sentences.

16. Explain the difference between tension and compression.

_____

_____

17. Why do many structural shapes include triangles? Give examples.

_____

_____

18. Explain the difference between a static load and a dynamic load.

_____

_____

19. Describe the use of studs, joists, and rafters in framing houses.

_____

_____

20. What structural member can take the place of joists and rafters in a structure?

_____

TECHNOLOGY INTERACTIONS Teacher's Resource Guide
Copyright © Glencoe/McGraw-Hill

Chapter Test   10

Flight

I. Using Vocabulary

Match each item in Column I with the most appropriate item in Column II. Write the letter for that item in the blank at the left.

Column I	Column II

Column I

_____ 1. a force that slows an object and eventually stops it

_____ 2. an object shaped to control the sped of air flowing over it

_____ 3. flaps that change the shape of an airplane wing to control lift

_____ 4. an upward force

_____ 5. a study that deals with the forces of air on an object as it moves through the air

_____ 6. a force that pulls objects toward the center of the Earth

_____ 7. a property of matter that causes it to remain still or continue to move in the same direction until an outside force acts on it

_____ 8. the force of fluid friction on moving objects

_____ 9. the cause of the resistance an object meets as it moves through the air

_____ 10. the forward force an airplane needs to fly

Column II

a. airfoil
b. drag
c. thrust
d. gravity
e. lift
f. friction
g. rudder
h. aerodynamics
i. inertia
j. ailerons
k. fluid friction

(continued next page)

II. Understanding Concepts and Applying Skills

Briefly describe Isaac Newton's three laws of motion.

11. First law: _____

_____

_____

12. Second law: _____

_____

_____

13. Third law: _____

_____

_____

Answer the following questions in phrases or complete sentences.

14. In what ways are the rotor blades on a helicopter and the propeller on an airplane the same?

_____

_____

_____

_____

15. Explain how the drag on a car can be reduced.

_____

_____

_____

_____

_____

(continued next page)

Chapter 10 Test (continued)

16. Describe how a jet engine works. To which law of motion does this apply?

_____

_____

_____

_____

_____

17. In what way does the mass of an object affect the force of gravity? Explain.

_____

_____

_____

_____

_____

18. Explain how the shape of an airplane's wings helps create lift.

_____

_____

_____

_____

_____

(continued next page)

19. Explain how a pilot controls a helicopter.

_____

_____

_____

_____

_____

_____

20. Describe the parts of an airplane that allow the pilot to control its direction.

_____

_____

_____

_____

_____

TECHNOLOGY INTERACTIONS Teacher's Resource Guide

Chapter Test   11

Land and Water Transportation

I. Using Vocabulary

Match each item in Column I with the most appropriate item in Column II. Write the letter for that item in the blank at the left.

Column I	Column II
_____ 1. water vehicle that transports people and products	a. vessel
_____ 2. internal-combustion engine that burns fuel oil using heat produced by compressing air	b. diesel engine
	c. transportation
_____ 3. engine that creates power by burning fuel inside the engine	d. external-combustion engine
_____ 4. upward force a fluid places on an object placed in it	e. maglev
	f. buoyancy
_____ 5. the process by which people, animals, products, and materials are moved from one place to another	g. vessel
_____ 6. train that is lifted and propelled by magnetic fields	

II. Understanding Concepts and Applying Skills

In the blank at the left, write the TRUE if the statement is true or FALSE if the statement is false.

_____ 7. The input in all transportation systems is energy.

_____ 8. Railroading on a wide scale became possible with the invention of all-electric locomotives.

_____ 9. Commuter train systems are often referred to as *mass transit*.

_____ 10. Maglev trains have electromagnetic engines.

_____ 11. All gasoline piston engines are heat engines, but not all heat engines are gasoline piston engines.

(continued next page)

Chapter 11 Test (continued)

_____ 12. A forklift that moves building supplies around a lumber-yard is an example of on-site transportation.

_____ 13. Tankers and freighters have displacement-style hulls.

_____ 14. The buoyancy of a boat depends on the type of material from which it is made.

_____ 15. Sails can be used to propel vessels into the wind.

Answer the following questions in phrases or complete sentences.

16. Why is rail travel becoming more attractive to travelers?

_____

_____

17. In what ways is the operation of a diesel engine different from the operation of a gasoline engine?

_____

_____

_____

18. Why does a boat float?

_____

_____

19. Suppose you were traveling in a car from Baltimore, Maryland to Washington, D.C. The distance is approximately 450 miles. If you made the trip in 7 hours and 30 minutes, what was your average speed?

_____

20. State officials are considering constructing a maglev train system between two large cities and an airport in your area. They have requested your input in making their decision. Would you speak for or against the project? Give reasons for your position.

_____

_____

_____

Chapter Test 12

Fluid Power

I. Using Vocabulary

Match each item in Column I with the most appropriate item in Column II. Write the letter for that item in the blank at the left.

Column I	Column II
_____ 1. fluid power systems that use oil or another liquid	a. pressure
_____ 2. fluid power systems that use air or another gas	b. hydraulic systems
	c. fluid power
_____ 3. the use of pressurized liquids or gases to move objects and perform other tasks	d. compression
	e. Pascal's Principle
_____ 4. increase in force gained by using a machine	f. pneumatic systems
_____ 5. force on a unit surface area	g. mechanical advantage
	h. fluid
_____ 6. when force is applied to a confined liquid, the resulting pressure is transmitted unchanged to all parts of the liquid	
_____ 7. any material that flows	

II. Understanding Concepts and Applying Skills

In the blank at the left, write the letter of the choice that best completes the statement.

_____ 8. The state of matter that can be compressed is
    a. solid.   b. liquid.   c. gas.   d. both b and c.

_____ 9. The amount of space a fluid occupies is its
    a. pressure.   b. volume.   c. force.   d. area.

_____ 10. What is the pressure (pounds per square inch) in a hydraulic system when a force of 8,000 pounds is applied to a piston with a surface area of 4 square inches? Use the following formula:

$$P = \frac{F}{A}$$

    a. 2,000 psi   b. 4,000 psi   c. 8,000 psi   d. 32,000 psi

(continued next page)

Chapter 12 Test (continued)

_____ 11. The fluid power component that changes pressure into mechanical motion is the
    a. actuator.   c. flow regulator.
    b. control valve.   d. transmission line.

Answer the following questions in phrases or complete sentences.

12. Why is the fact that fluids can flow important in a fluid power system?

_____

_____

13. Why can gases be compressed but liquids and solids cannot?

_____

_____

14. Identify the components of a fluid power system and briefly tell the basic purpose of each.

_____

_____

_____

_____

_____

15. Why is a bicycle pump not really a "pump"?

_____

_____

*Listed below are tasks performed by fluid power systems in various industries. For each task, tell whether a hydraulic or pneumatic system would most likely be used by writing **H** for hydraulic or **P** for pneumatic.*

_____ 16. painting a car

_____ 17. lowering the landing gear on an airplane

_____ 18. using a crane to lift construction materials

_____ 19. canning food

_____ 20. raising a dental chair

Chapter Test 13

Health Technologies

I. Using Vocabulary

Match each item in Column I with the most appropriate item in Column II. Write the letter for that item in the blank at the left.

Column I

_____ 1. the design process that gives special attention to the strengths and limitations of the human body

_____ 2. process of examining a patient and studying the symptoms to find out what illness a patient has

_____ 3. an action that protects the body against a disease

_____ 4. the study of designing equipment and devices that fit the human body, its movement, and its thinking patterns

_____ 5. a people-made device that gives special attention to the strengths and limitations of the human body

_____ 6. process of changing genetic materials that make up living organisms

_____ 7. the use of engineering principles and design procedures to solve medical problems

Column II

a. genetic engineering
b. ergonomics
c. human factors engineering
d. prosthesis
e. diagnosis
f. material processes
g. biomechanical engineering
h. immunization

I. Understanding Concepts and Applying Skills

In the blank at the left, write the TRUE if the statement is true or FALSE if the statement is false.

_____ 8. A replacement knee joint would most likely be designed by a biomechanical engineer.

_____ 9. Prostheses can be used to replace many body parts but not the internal organs.

(continued next page)

_____ 10. Although electronic devices are not widely used as physical enhancement aids at the present time, it is believed that they will be used a great deal in the future.

_____ 11. The body's natural defense system is its immune system.

_____ 12. Vaccines are substances placed in the body to increase its immunity to various diseases artificially.

_____ 13. Using the genetic material of one individual to develop an identical individual is called *prototyping*.

_____ 14. A human factors engineer deals with ergonomic designs.

Answer the following questions in phrases or complete sentences.

15. Identify five technological activities associated with health technologies.

_____

_____

16. Briefly describe a typical workday for a biomechanical engineer.

_____

_____

17. What are the two major human technology resources? Why are they important?

_____

_____

18. Explain how technology has improved diagnostic techniques.

_____

_____

19. What progress do you expect to be made in bio-related technology in the future?

_____

_____

20. What might a human factors engineer need to consider when designing a kitchen for use by a person in a wheelchair?

_____

Chapter Test

14

Environmental Technologies

I. Using Vocabulary

Match each item in Column I with the most appropriate item in Column II. Write the letter for that item in the blank at the left.

Column I

_____ 1. tiny particle that carries genes

_____ 2. science that studies the laws of heredity

_____ 3. process plants use to convert sunlight to energy

_____ 4. using living microorganisms to change materials

_____ 5. technology of producing perfect growing conditions for plants

_____ 6. study of the passing on of traits from parents to offspring

_____ 7. combining traits of one animal with those of another animal

_____ 8. improving techniques used to nurture life

_____ 9. introduction of genes from one cell to another cell

_____ 10. growing plants in a soilless environment

Column II

a. bioprocessing
b. genetics
c. genetic engineering
d. chromosome
e. photosynthesis
f. heredity
g. controlled environment agriculture (CEA)
h. hydroponics
i. traditional soil farming
j. bio-related technology
k. selective breeding

II. Understanding Concepts and Applying Skills

In the blank at the left, write the TRUE if the statement is true or FALSE if the statement is false.

_____ 11. Mechanization is a bio-related technology that is responsible for great increases in agricultural production.

_____ 12. A bee that carries pollen from one flower to another flower is participating in the process of pollination.

(continued next page)

Chapter 14 Test (continued)

_____ 13. Chromosomes are arranged like beads on a string around genes in the nucleus of a cell.

_____ 14. In a hydroponic system, if plants are fed the proper nutrients in water, they can be raised in total darkness.

_____ 15. A biosphere could be used to grow food crops in deserts because it contains everything needed for life.

Answer the following questions in phrases or complete sentences.

16. How has mechanization affected the performance of the activities involved in growing crops?

_____

_____

_____

17. How can plants be reproduced without seeds or pollination?

_____

_____

18. Explain briefly how bioprocessing techniques can be used to benefit the environment.

_____

_____

19. In 1860, the population of the United States was about 40,500,000. As an average, approximately two people in farming provided food for three people. In 1996, the population of the United States was about 264,000,000. As an average (just in the United States), how many people was each person in farming responsible for feeding? (Round off to the nearest whole number.)

_____

20. Do you think it is important or not important for us to learn to grow crops in space? Give reasons for your opinion.

_____

_____

_____

Chapter Test

15

Electricity and Electronics

I. Using Vocabulary

Match each item in Column I with the most appropriate item in Column II. Write the letter for that item in the blank at the left.

Column I

_____ 1. movement of electrons from atom to another

_____ 2. flow of electrons through a conductor

_____ 3. pathway through which electrons travel

_____ 4. force that causes electrons to flow

_____ 5. device that converts chemical energy into electrical energy

_____ 6. statement of the mathematical relationship between current, voltage, and resistance

_____ 7. relationship between electricity and magnetism

_____ 8. opposition to the flow of electrons

_____ 9. semiconductor device that amplifies and acts as an electronic switch

_____ 10. device that changes mechanical energy into electrical energy

Column II

a. Ohm's law
b. battery
c. law of charges
d. resistance
e. circuit
f. potential difference
g. transistor
h. electromagnetism
i. current
j. electricity
k. generator

II. Understanding Concepts and Applying Skills

In the blank at the left, write the TRUE if the statement is true or FALSE if the statement is false.

_____ 11. Potential difference, voltage, and electromotive force are all terms that refer to the force that causes electrons to flow.

_____ 12. Electrons flow through a conductor from the negative end to the positive end.

(continued next page)

_____ 13. Wires used to carry electricity are often covered with plastic because plastic is a good conductor.

_____ 14. To work effectively, electricity must flow continuously in one direction.

Answer the following questions in phrases or complete sentences.

15. Describe voltage, current, and resistance and explain the role each plays in the production of electricity we can use.

_____

_____

_____

_____

_____

16. a. What is Ohm's law?

_____

_____

b. What formula states the law mathematically?

c. Using Ohm's law, calculate the rate of current flow through a 120-volt circuit with a resistance of 20 ohms.

_____

_____

d. Rewrite the formula to solve for resistance.

(continued next page)

17. a. What is the difference between a series circuit and a parallel circuit?

_____

_____

_____

   b. In the space below, make a drawing of a parallel circuit. Show the power source and show one lightbulb in each path of current flow.

18. How are electricity and electronics different?

_____

_____

_____

_____

_____

(continued next page)

Chapter 15 Test (continued)

19. What result would you expect if the base current entering a transistor is increased slightly? Explain.

_____

_____

_____

_____

_____

20. Describe the operation of a transistor radio in terms of input, process, and output. Is there a feedback element? Explain.

_____

_____

_____

_____

_____

_____

_____

Chapter Test   16

Computer Control Systems

I. Using Vocabulary

Match each item in Column I with the most appropriate item in Column II. Write the letter for that item in the blank at the left.

Column I

_____ 1. software that provides tools for drawing and dimensioning a product

_____ 2. software that can test a product design by simulating the environment in which the product must be able to work

_____ 3. a system that uses computers to control the operation of machines during production

_____ 4. letter-number combinations used in a CNC program that locates points for machine operations in manufacturing a product

_____ 5. using computers to manufacture a product

_____ 6. a combination of computer-aided design and computer-aided manufacturing

_____ 7. a system that allows the manufacturer to make a variety of designs using the same machines

Column II

a. simulation software
b. CAD/CAM
c. Cartesian coordinates
d. flexible manufacturing system
e. just-in-time manufacturing
f. computer-aided manufacturing
g. computer-aided design
h. computer numerical control

II. Understanding Concepts and Applying Skills

In the blank at the left, write the TRUE if the statement is true or FALSE if the statement is false.

_____ 8. CAD programs automatically calculate dimensions for the object being drawn.

_____ 9. CAD programs can be used with CAM programs but not with engineering programs.

(continued next page)

_____ 10. Animation software enables designers to view realistic images of new design concepts in action.

_____ 11. A milling machine is used to shape rounded objects such as baseball bats.

_____ 12. In numerical control systems, instructions are input into machines in the form of codes.

_____ 13. Manual data input is the process of inputting information directly into machines on the manufacturing floor.

_____ 14. Most CNC machines use only three axes to locate points on a workpiece, but complicated parts may require more.

_____ 15. Coordinates are workstations consisting of computer-controlled machines that can perform a variety of operations.

Write the terms represented by the following abbreviations and give a brief description of each.

16. a. CAD _____

_____

_____

b. CAM _____

_____

_____

c. CNC _____

_____

_____

d. FMS _____

_____

_____

e. MDI _____

_____

_____

(continued next page)

Chapter 16 Test (continued)

17. To which Cartesian coordinates does the following machine program code refer? GOOX.2Z.3F4

_____

18. Describe three advantages of using CAD/CAM systems in manufacturing.

_____

_____

_____

_____

_____

_____

19. Suppose you are a manufacturer. Refer to item 16 on the previous page and briefly tell how you would use each of the computer control systems listed to produce products.

_____

_____

_____

_____

_____

_____

_____

_____

_____

_____

(continued next page)

20. Plot the following X,Y points on the graph paper provided. Remember, the first co-ordinate given always refers to the X axis, and the second always refers to the Y axis. Connect the points plotted for each shape with straight lines. What product have you drawn?

_____

Shape 1	Shape 2	Shape 3	Shape 4	Shape 5	Shape 6
(–5,5)	(–5,–5)	(–4,4)	(–4,–6)	(1,–6)	(–3,–4)
(5,5)	(5,–5)	(4,4)	(–1,–6)	(4,–6)	(–3,–5)
Line ends	Line ends	Line ends	Line ends	Line ends	Line ends
(5,5)	(5,–5)	(4,4)	(–1,–6)	(4,–6)	(3,–4)
(5,–4)	(5,–8)	(4,–3)	(–1,–7)	(4,–7)	(3,–5)
Line ends	Line ends	Line ends	Line ends	Line ends	Line ends
(5,–4)	(5,–8)	(4,–3)	(–1,–7)	(4,–7)	End drawing
(5,5)	(5,–5)	(4,4)	(–1,–6)	(4,–6)	
Line ends	Line ends	Line ends	Line ends	Line ends	
(–5,–4)	(–5,–8)	(–4,–3)	(–4,–7)	(1,–7)	
Line ends	Line ends	Line ends	Line ends	Line ends	
(–5,–4)	(–5,–8)	(–4,–3)	(–4,–7)	(1,–7)	
(–5,5)	(–5,–5)	(–4,4)	(–4,–6)	(1,–6)	
Line ends	Line ends	Line ends	Line ends	Line ends	

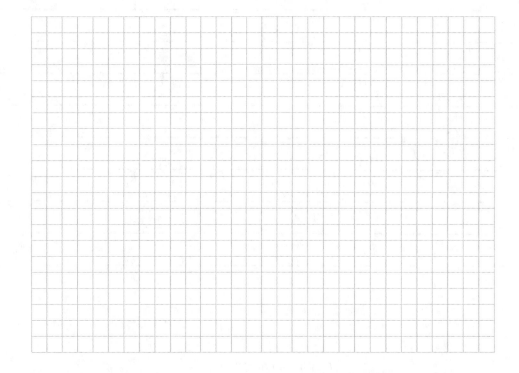

TECHNOLOGY INTERACTIONS Teacher's Resource Guide
Copyright © Glencoe/McGraw-Hill

Name _____ Class _____ Date _____

Chapter Test 17

Robotics

I. Using Vocabulary

Match each item in Column I with the most appropriate item in Column II. Write the letter for that item in the blank at the left.

Column I

_____ 1. the study of robots

_____ 2. space within which a robotic arm moves

_____ 3. ability of a robot to move in a direction

_____ 4. a machine made to act like a living thing

_____ 5. technique used to make a process automatic

_____ 6. process of sending signals, interpreting received signals, and adjusting through signals

Column II

a. robotics
b. stepper motor
c. degree of freedom
d. automation
e. work envelope
f. feedback control
g. robot

II. Understanding Concepts and Applying Skills

In the blank at the left, write the TRUE if the statement is true or FALSE if the statement is false.

_____ 7. Robotics is a control system technology.

_____ 8. The first computers were desktop calculators.

_____ 9. Computer-controlled machine tools are not robots.

_____ 10. Robotic hands called *end effectors* are often changed to suit the task.

_____ 11. Robotic programs are simple outlines of the major movements the robots must make.

_____ 12. Robots use various types of actuators to feed information back to a computer about a task on which it is working.

_____ 13. The motors that control the robotic arm's movements are turned on and off using coded electrical signals.

(continued next page)

Chapter 17 Test (continued)

Answer the following questions in phrases or complete sentences.

14. To participate in surgery, a robot must be accurate and steady. What features do you think would be needed by a robot gathering data on the surface of another planet?

_____

_____

15. Why was Herman Hollerith's invention of the punch card tabulating machine in the 1800s essential to later developments in computer control technology?

_____

_____

16. Describe some ways in which robotic systems are like human systems.

_____

_____

17. How are stepper motors used to create a variety of robotic movements?

_____

_____

18. Calculate the volume of the work envelope for a person with a reach of 21 inches. (Use the formula for calculating the volume of a sphere: $V = \frac{4}{3}\pi r^3$)

_____

_____

19. What is lead-through programming? Why is this type of programming useful?

_____

_____

20. What are the two major types of sensors that robots use to gather information to send back to the computer? A camera is an example of which type of sensor?

_____

_____

_____

Chapter Test   18

Lasers and Fiber Optics

I. Using Vocabulary

Match each item in Column I with the most appropriate item in Column II. Write the letter for that item in the blank at the left.

Column I

_____ 1. wave produced by the motion of electrically charged particles

_____ 2. light that consists of one color

_____ 3. light that spreads out very little

_____ 4. light source that sends out light in a narrow, strong beam

_____ 5. light in which all of the light waves have the same wavelength

_____ 6. photographic process that uses a laser, lenses, and mirrors to produce three-dimensional images

_____ 7. a tiny unit of energy

Column II

a. monochromatic light
b. laser
c. electromagnetic wave
d. photon
e. excitation mechanism
f. directional light
g. coherent light
h. holography

II. Understanding Concepts and Applying Skills

In the blank at the left, write the TRUE if the statement is true or FALSE if the statement is false.

_____ 8. The light that we see is produced by millions of photons.

_____ 9. Extremely bright rainbow colors are produced when a laser beam is split by passing it through water.

_____ 10. Electromagnetic radiation is another term for laser light.

_____ 11. Forms of electromagnetic waves are classified by wavelength.

(continued next page)

Chapter 18 Test (continued)

_____ 12. Sunlight is monochromatic light.

_____ 13. Light from an ordinary lightbulb is incoherent light.

_____ 14. The term *laser* is short for "Light Amplification by Stimulated Radar."

_____ 15. The light from a laser can be continuous or given off in short pulses.

Answer the following questions in phrases or complete sentences.

16. Explain how laser light is different from ordinary light.

_____

_____

17. Which part of the body is, perhaps, the most susceptible to damage from lasers and yet is greatly benefited by today's surgical procedures?

_____

18. Identify the three subsystems of a laser system and explain how they work together to produce a laser beam.

_____

_____

_____

19. How are holograms different from photographs? How might they be more useful than photographs in your studies at school? Give an example.

_____

_____

_____

_____

20. Select two industries and tell how lasers are used in those industries. Include ideas for how lasers might be used in the future.

_____

_____

_____

Chapter Test 19

Engineering

I. Using Vocabulary

Match each item in Column I with the most appropriate item in Column II. Write the letter for that item in the blank at the left.

Column I

_____ 1. a problem solving process and a design process

_____ 2. a person who uses his or her knowledge of science, technology, and mathematics to solve technical problems

_____ 3. a process used to develop solutions to problems

_____ 4. rules or models against which a product, action, or process can be compared

Column II

a. engineering
b. engineering process
c. standards
d. architect
e. engineer

II. Understanding Concepts and Applying Skills

Answer the following questions in phrases or complete sentences.

5. List the steps in the engineering process in order.

_____

_____

_____

6. You have been asked to design a new type of clipboard. Using the engineering process, tell you you would proceed in solving this design problem.

_____

_____

_____

(continued next page)

7. Which type of engineering or related occupation appeals to you most? Select one and explain the type of work and tasks performed by a person in that occupation. Then explain why you selected that occupation.

_____

_____

_____

_____

Listed in Column I below are various types of tasks performed by engineers and people whose work is closely related. Select from column II the type of engineer or other worker you would hire to perform each task. Write the letter of the occupation on the lines beside the numbers of the tasks to be performed. Two items have two answers. Occupations may be used more than once. All occupations will be used.

Column I	**Column II**
_____ 8. design and build a government building	a. aerospace engineer
_____ 9. oversee all operations in a printing plant	b. architect
_____ 10. design and organize machine placements on an assembly line	c. chemical engineer
	d. civil engineer
_____ 11. improve the design of a mousetrap	e. computer engineer
_____ 12. design a part for a machine	f. electrical/electronics engineer
_____ 13. design the frame of a new type of aircraft	g. environmental engineer
_____ 14. design a new school building	h. industrial designer
_____ 15. design a circuit for a VCR	i. manufacturing engineer
_____ 16. design and manage the processes used to remove iron ore from the ground	j. materials engineer
_____ 17. develop a heat-resistant material to use in making parts for a heating system	k. mechanical engineer
	l. mining engineer
_____ 18. design software for a company's operations	m. systems engineer
_____ 19. design the vessels in which chemical reactions take place	
_____ 20. design a system to clean up a polluted area	

Name _____ Class _____ Date _____

Chapter Test   20

Applied Physics

I. Using Vocabulary

Match each item in Column I with the most appropriate item in Column II. Write the letter for that item in the blank at the left.

Column I

_____ 1. a push or pull applied to an object

_____ 2. the study of the ways in which objects are moved and work is done

_____ 3. the force of attraction that exists between two objects

_____ 4. the number of times a machine multiplies a force

_____ 5. the tendency of an object to continue to move or to stay at rest

_____ 6. the application of force to cause an object to move in the direction of the force

_____ 7. the rate at which work is done or how much work is accomplished in a certain period of time

_____ 8. a force that opposes motion

_____ 9. a device designed to obtain the greatest amount of force from the energy used

Column II

a. work
b. inertia
c. gravity
d. friction
e. mechanical advantage
f. applied physics
g. force
h. power
i. escape velocity
j. machine

II. Understanding Concepts and Applying Skills

In the blank at the left, write the TRUE if the statement is true or FALSE if the statement is false.

_____ 10. The more aerodynamic the shape of a vehicle, the greater the drag the vehicle encounters as it moves.

_____ 11. The rate at which an object moves depends on the size of the force acting on it and the object's mass.

(continued next page)

Chapter 20 Test (continued)

_____ 12. A force strong enough to cause an object to move or change direction is a reaction force.

_____ 13. All forces occur in pairs.

_____ 14. If a person tries to lift an object but is unable to move it, no work has been done.

_____ 15. Electromagnetic waves are light waves only if we can see them.

Answer the following questions in phrases or complete sentences.

16. List in order the steps in the scientific method.

_____

_____

_____

17. Explain the forces acting on a thrown ball.

_____

_____

18. What are Newton's three laws of motion?

_____

_____

_____

19. List the six simple machines. Which type of simple machine is a crowbar used for prying?

_____

_____

_____

20. Suppose you and a friend are planning to take a walk in the vacuum of outer space. For security reasons, you cannot communicate by radio. Would you choose a clicker to send sound signals or a flashlight to send light signals? Explain your choice scientifically in terms of how sound and light waves travel.

_____

_____

Answer Key for Career Activity Masters

The following answers are brief and are intended as guidelines only. Student answers may vary with current industry trends and student sources. Note that all income figures are yearly sums. Answers to the "What do YOU think?" questions for each career will vary depending on student preferences and are therefore not included in this answer key.

CAREER ACTIVITY 1

Industrial Production Manager

1. Industrial production managers coordinate the resources and activities required to produce millions of goods every year.
2. About 206,000; 50% are employed in industrial, transportation, or electronic and electrical equipment, fabricated metal products, or food products manufacturing.
3. bachelor's degree
4. slower than average
5. about $63,000

Computer Scientist

1. Computer scientists design computers, conduct research to improve design or use, and develop or adapt principles for applying computers to new uses.
2. Computer scientists and systems analysts hold about 828,000 jobs. Although they are found in most industries, the greatest concentration is in the computer and data processing services industry.
3. bachelor's degree
4. faster than average
5. about $44,000

Data Processing Manager

1. Data processing managers direct, plan, and coordinate data processing activities to reach goals.
2. About 337,000; although they are found in almost all industries, nearly two-fifths are employed in manufacturing.
3. bachelor's degree
4. faster than average
5. starting income: $35,000.

Engineering Manager

1. Engineering managers direct and coordinate production, operations, quality assurance, testing, or maintenance in industrial plants. They may also plan or coordinate the design and development of machinery products, systems, and processes.
2. About 337,000
3. bachelor's degree
4. faster than average
5. median income for lower-level engineering managers: $78,100

Industrial Engineering Technician

1. Industrial engineering technicians use principles of science, engineering, and mathematics to solve technical problems in manufacturing.
2. Engineering technicians (including industrial engineering technicians) hold about 685,000 jobs. About 40% work in manufacturing; nearly 25% work in service industries.
3. associate degree
4. slower than average
5. median income (lower-level): $16,590

Operations Manager

1. Managers of communication, transportation, and utilities operations facilities plan, organize, direct, control, or coordinate management activities related to their specific industries.
2. About 154,000 operations managers are employed in the communication, transportation, and utilities industries.
3. bachelor's degree
4. slower than average
5. no data available

Construction and Building Inspector

1. Construction and building inspectors examine the construction, alteration, or repair of buildings, highways and streets, sewer and water systems, dams, bridges, and other structures to ensure compliance with building codes and ordinances, zoning regulations, and contract specifications.
2. About 64,000; more than 50% in local governments, primarily municipal or counting building departments.
3. Other; inspectors usually receive most of their training on the job, although some formal training is helpful. They need several years of experience as a manager, supervisor, or craft worker before becoming an inspector.
4. faster than average
5. median income: $32,300

Biological Scientist

1. Biological scientists study living organisms and their relationship to their environment. They use technology to manipulate the genetic materials of animals or plants to make organisms more productive or disease-resistant.
2. Biological and medical scientists hold about 118,000 jobs. Almost 1 in 3 non-faculty biological scientists are employed by federal, state, or local governments. Most of the rest work for pharmaceutical and biotechnology establishments, hospitals, or research and testing laboratories.
3. master's degree
4. faster than average
5. median income: $37,500

CAREER ACTIVITY 2

Urban and Regional Planner

1. Urban and regional planners develop long- and short-term land use plans for growth and revitalization of urban, suburban, and rural communities.
2. About 29,000; about two-thirds are employed by local governments.
3. bachelor's degree
4. faster than average
5. about $30,000 to $37,000

Marketing Research Analyst

1. Marketing research analysts analyze statistical data on past sales to predict future sales and make recommendations based on their findings.
2. About 48,000 (1994); private industry employed 80% of salaried workers.
3. bachelor's degree
4. faster than average
5. about $25,400 (1995)

Systems Analyst

1. Systems analysts apply their knowledge of computer technology to implement solutions that meet the individual needs of an organization.
2. About 828,000 jobs; the greatest concentration is in the computer and data processing services industry.
3. bachelor's degree
4. faster than average
5. Starting salaries in large establishments range from $43,500 to $54,000; in smaller establishments, they range from $35,000 to $45,000.

Consumer Safety Inspector

1. Consumer safety inspectors inspect food, feeds and pesticides, weights and measures, biological products, cosmetics, drugs and medical equipment, and radiation-emitting products.
2. About 157,000; state and local governments employ about 52%; the rest work in the private sector.
3. bachelor's degree
4. same as average
5. Median income is $34,680, but wages vary depending on the nature of the inspection or compliance activity.

Engineer

1. Engineers apply the theories and principles of science and mathematics to the economical solution of practical technical problems, often linking scientific discoveries with their commercial applications.
2. About 1,327,000; 47% work in manufacturing industries, and the remaining jobs are primarily in services in which firms work on a contract basis for organizations in other parts of the economy.
3. bachelor's degree
4. same as average
5. about $34,100

Industrial Designer

1. Industrial designers develop and design manufactured products such as cars, toys, home appliances, and computer, medical, office, and recreational equipment.
2. About 301,000; most industrial designers work for consulting firms or for large corporations.
3. bachelor's degree
4. faster than average
5. about $25,800

CAREER ACTIVITY 3

Architect

1. Architects design buildings, structures, and their surroundings to satisfy clients' functional and aesthetic requirements. Architects are increasingly turning to CAD technology in their work.
2. About 91,000; most jobs were in architectural firms.
3. bachelor's degree
4. same as average
5. $24,700

Electronics Engineer

1. Electronics engineers design, develop, test, and supervise the manufacture of electrical and electronic equipment such as radar, computer hardware, and communication and video equipment. Many engineers use CAD systems to increase the speed and accuracy with which they work.
2. About 349,000; most jobs were in engineering and business consulting firms, manufacturers of electrical and electronic equipment, professional and scientific instruments, and government agencies.
3. bachelor's degree
4. same as average
5. starting income: $34,840

(continued next page)

TECHNOLOGY INTERACTIONS Teacher's Resource Guide

Drafter

1. Drafters prepare detailed technical drawings that enable workers to manufacture products or construct projects. Many drafters use CAD systems to prepare their drawings.
2. About 304,000; more than 33% work in engineering and architectural services on a contract basis; another 33% work in durable goods manufacturing industries; most of the others work in construction, communication, utilities, or personal supply services.
3. associate degree
4. same as average
5. median income: $28,500

Electrical Drafter

1. Electrical drafters draw wiring and layout diagrams used by workers who erect, install, and repair electrical equipment and wiring in power plants, electrical distribution systems, and buildings. Many drafters use CAD systems to prepare their drawings.
2. About 304,000; see "Drafter" entry above for details.
3. associate degree
4. same as average
5. median income: $28,500

Engineering Technician

1. Engineering technicians use principles of science, engineering, and mathematics to solve technical problems in research and development, manufacturing, sales, construction, and customer service. They often use CAD equipment.
2. Engineering technicians hold about 685,000 jobs. About 40% work in manufacturing; nearly 25% work in service industries.
3. associate degree
4. slower than average
5. median income at the junior level: $16,590.

Tool Programmers

1. Tool programmers analyze blueprints, compute size and position of cuts, determine sequence of machine operations, select tools, and calculate machine speed and feed rates. They then write computer programs to control the tools. A growing number of firms employ CAD systems to assist in writing the programs.
2. About 376,000; most work in small machining shops or in manufacturing firms that produce durable goods.
3. other: apprenticeship/vocational or technical school/post-secondary education
4. slower than average
5. median income: $27,040

CAREER ACTIVITY 4

Graphic Artist

1. Graphic artists use a variety of print, electronic, and film media to create art that meets clients' needs. Most graphic artists use computer software to design new images.
2. Visual artists, including graphic artists, number about 273,000. About 60% are self-employed, and the rest are employed by the motion picture or television industry or by advertising agencies, design firms, commercial art and reproduction firms, or publishing firms.
3. bachelor's degree
4. faster than average
5. entry-level: $21,000 to $24,000

Writer/Editor

1. Writers develop original fiction and nonfiction books, magazines and trade journals, newspapers, technical reports, radio and television broadcasts, movies, and advertisements. Editors select and prepare materials for publication. Their primary duties are to plan the contents of books, magazines, or newspapers and to supervise their preparation.
2. About 272,000; nearly 33% work for newspapers, magazines, and book publishers. Others are divided among the categories listed in question 1.
3. bachelor's degree
4. faster than average
5. entry-level income for writers and editorial assistants: $18,000; income for writers in the federal government: about $44,000.

Photographer/Camera Operator

1. Photographers and camera operators capture the special feeling or mood that sells products, provides entertainment, highlights news stories, or brings back memories. A photographer may take a picture, scan it to digital form, and use a computer to manipulate it to create desired special effects.
2. About 139,000, including photographers and camera operators; about 40% are self-employed. Most salaried photographers work in portrait or commercial photography studios or at newspapers, magazines, advertising agencies, and government agencies.
3. bachelor's degree
4. faster than average
5. median income: $25,100

Word Processor

1. Word processors set up and enter reports, letters, mailing labels, and other text material using computers and other electronic equipment.

(continued next page)

2. Nearly 1.1 million; they are employed in every sector of the economy.
3. other: high-school graduate with word processing or data entry training
4. slower than average
5. median income: $22,900

CAREER ACTIVITY 5

Animator

1. Animators draw by hand and use computers to create the large series of pictures that, when transferred to film or tape, form the animated cartoons seen in movies and on television. Duties may vary from mechanical work such as paste-up to more advanced work such as creating original designs and layout.
2. About 273,000 visual artists, which includes animators; animators work in the motion picture and television industries.
3. bachelor's degree
4. faster than average
5. median income: $25,500 per year

Illustrator

1. Illustrators paint or draw pictures for books and other publications, films, and other applications. Some illustrators draw storyboards for television commercials, movies, and animated features.
2. About 273,000 visual artists, including illustrators; approximately 60% are self-employed. Others work for advertising agencies, design firms, commercial art and reproduction firms, publishers, or the motion picture and television industries.
3. bachelor's degree
4. faster than average
5. median income: $25,500

Computer Programmer

1. Computer programmers write, test, and maintain the detailed constructions, called *programs* or *software,* that list in a logical order the steps that computers must execute to perform their functions.
2. About 573,000; they are employed in most industries, but the largest concentrations are in data processing service organizations.
3. bachelor's degree
4. same as average
5. entry-level income in large companies: $33,000; in smaller companies: $29,500; in the federal government: $18,700

Computer Scientist/Computer Engineer

1. Computer scientists and engineers generally design computers and conduct research to improve their design or use for particular purposes.

2. About 828,000; although they are found in most industries, the greatest concentration of jobs is in the computer and data processing services industries. Many others work for government agencies, computer manufacturers, insurance companies, and universities.
3. bachelor's degree
4. faster than average
5. median income: $44,000

CAREER ACTIVITY 6

Librarian/Media Specialist

1. Librarians help people find information and use it effectively. Use of the Internet and other worldwide computer systems is expanding the amount of available reference information. Librarians must be increasingly aware of how to use these resources to locate information.
2. About 148,000; most are in school and academic libraries; others are in public and special libraries.
3. master's degree
4. slower than average
5. median income: $35,600

Library Technician/Media Assistant

1. Library technicians help librarians acquire, prepare, and organize materials and help users find materials and information. Technicians may also instruct patrons on how to use computer systems and access data.
2. About 75,000; most work in school, academic, or public libraries.
3. associate degree
4. same as average
5. Income for library technicians varies greatly depending on the type of library and the geographic location. Income for those in the federal government averages $25,100.

Computer Programmer

1. Computer programmers write, test, and maintain the detailed constructions, called *programs* or *software,* that list in a logical order the steps that computers must execute to perform their functions. The Internet is one area of specialization for programmers in database development and web security.
2. About 573,000; they are employed in most industries, but the largest concentrations are in data processing service organizations.
3. bachelor's degree
4. same as average
5. entry-level income in large companies: $33,000; in smaller companies: $29,500; in the federal government: $18,700

(continued next page)

Database Administrator

1. Database administrators work with database management software to reorganize and restructure data to suit the needs of users. They serve an essential role for the Internet in preparing servers for use.
2. About 573,000 computer programmers, including database administrators; they are employed in most industries, but the largest concentrations are in data processing service organizations.
3. bachelor's degree
4. same as average
5. entry-level income in large companies: $33,000; in smaller companies: $29,500; in the federal government: $18,700

Computer Support Analyst

1. Computer support analysts provide assistance and advice to users, interpreting problems and providing technical support for hardware, software, and systems. Internet service providers hire computer support analysts to provide customer support and guidance.
2. About 573,000 computer programmers, including computer support analysts; they are employed in most industries, but the largest concentrations are in data processing service organizations.
3. bachelor's degree
4. same as average
5. entry-level income in large companies: $33,000; in smaller companies: $29,500; in the federal government: $18,700

Service/Sales Representative

1. Service/sales representatives act as industry experts, consultants, and problem solvers when selling their firm's services. Internet sales is a new area in which salespeople sell access accounts for Internet service providers. Some Internet sales representatives may also specialize in selling Web space to companies. Others sell advertising on the Web site.
2. More than 612,000 jobs; over half are in firms that provide business services, including computer and data processing.
3. bachelor's degree
4. faster than average
5. entry-level income: $27,800

CAREER ACTIVITY 7

Broadcast Technician

1. Broadcast technicians install, test, repair, set up, and operate the electronic equipment used to record and transmit radio and television programs.
2. About 42,000; most work in radio and television

broadcasting. The rest work in the motion picture industry or for cable and other pay television services.
3. associate degree
4. slower than average
5. entry level at radio stations: $23,560; at television stations: $24,260

Recording Engineer

1. Recording engineers set up and operate video and sound recording equipment, including special effects equipment.
2. About 42,000 broadcast technicians, including recording engineers; most work in radio and television broadcasting. The rest work in the motion picture industry or for cable and other pay television services.
3. associate degree
4. slower than average
5. entry-level at radio stations: $23,560; at television stations: $24,260

Sound Mixer

1. Sound mixers (also called recording mixers) work in teams to produce the sound track of a movie using a process called dubbing. They follow a script that tells at precisely what moment, as the film runs through the projector, each sound must be faded in and out. All sounds for each shot are thus blended on a master sound track.
2. About 42,000 broadcast technicians, including sound mixers; most work in the motion picture industry.
3. associate degree
4. same as average
5. entry-level income: $20,000

Camera Operator

1. Camera operators use 35- or 16-millimeter cameras or video cameras to film commercial motion pictures and documentary or industrial films.
2. About 139,000 (camera operators and photographers); most camera operators are employed in television broadcasting or in motion picture studios.
3. associate degree
4. slower than average
5. median income: $25,100

Reporter

1. Reporters gather information and prepare stories that inform us about local, state, national, and international events; present points of view on current issues; and report on the actions of public officials, corporate executives, and special-interest groups.
2. About 59,000; most work for newspapers; others work in radio or television broadcasting or for magazines and wire services.

(continued next page)

3. bachelor's degree
4. slower than average
5. median income for newspaper reporters: $23,000; for radio reporters: $23,600; for television reporters: $31,240

Announcer

1. Radio announcers (disc jockeys), select and introduce recorded music; present news, sports, weather, and commercials; interview guests; and report on matters of community interest.
2. About 50,000 radio and television announcers and newscasters; nearly all are staff announcers at radio and television stations.
3. associate degree
4. same as average
5. median income for radio news announcer: $27,900; starting income for television announcers in small markets: $24,935

CAREER ACTIVITY 8

Industrial Engineer

1. Industrial engineers determine the most effective ways for an organization to use the basic factors of production—people, machines, materials, information, and energy—to make or process a product.
2. About 115,000; about 75% are in manufacturing industries.
3. bachelor's degree
4. same as average
5. entry-level income: $33,270

Mechanical Engineer

1. Mechanical engineers plan and design tools, engines, machines, and other mechanical equipment.
2. About 231,000; more than 60% work in manufacturing. The rest work in business and engineering consulting services and government agencies.
3. bachelor's degree
4. same as average
5. Entry-level income: $35,000

Industrial Production Manager

1. Industrial production managers coordinate the resources and activities required to produce goods; they are responsible for production scheduling, staffing, equipment, quality control, inventory control, and coordination of production activities with activities of other departments.
2. About 206,000; employment is distributed throughout the manufacturing industries.
3. bachelor's degree
4. slower than average
5. median income: $63,000

Occupational Safety and Health Inspector

1. Occupational safety and health inspectors visit places of employment to detect unsafe machinery and equipment or unhealthy working conditions. They discuss their findings with the employer or plant manager and order that violations be corrected promptly in accordance with federal, state, or local safety standards and regulations.
2. Inspectors and compliance officers, which include occupational safety and health inspectors, hold about 157,000 jobs; most are employed by federal, state, or local governments or the U.S. Postal Service.
3. bachelor's degree
4. same as average
5. entry-level income: $46,730; median income varies from $18,700 to $41,000, depending on the nature of the inspection

Industrial Buyer

1. Industrial buyers purchase goods and services for use by their organizations. To be effective, they must have a working technical knowledge of the goods or services to be purchased.
2. About 621,000; about 25% work in manufacturing and 50% in wholesale and retail trade establishments such as grocery or department stores.
3. bachelor's degree
4. slower than average
5. median income: $31,700

Industrial Machinery Repair

1. Industrial machinery repairers maintain and repair machinery in plants and factories. Often called maintenance mechanics, they spend much of their time doing preventive maintenance.
2. About 464,000; about 70% work in manufacturing industries. Others work for government agencies, public utilities, mining companies, and other businesses that rely on machinery.
3. apprenticeship
4. slower than average
5. median income: $27,560

CAREER ACTIVITY 9

Architect

1. Architects design buildings, structures, and their surroundings to satisfy clients' functional and aesthetic requirements.
2. About 91,000; most work in architectural firms.
3. bachelor's degree
4. same as average
5. entry-level income: $34,840

(continued next page)

TECHNOLOGY INTERACTIONS Teacher's Resource Guide

Civil Engineering Technician

1. Civil engineering technicians help civil engineers plan and build highways, buildings, bridges, dams, wastewater treatment systems, and other structures.
2. About 685,000, including civil engineering technicians; about 40% work in manufacturing, and 25% work in service industries. Most of the rest are employed by federal, state, and local governments.
3. associate degree
4. slower than average
5. median income at junior level: $16,590

Construction Manager

1. Construction managers typically schedule and co-ordinate all design and construction processes. They develop and implement a plan to complete the project according to the owner's goals.
2. About 197,000; more than 85% are employed in the construction industry.
3. bachelor's degree/other: substantial experience as a construction craft worker
4. faster than average
5. Median entry-level income: $30,000

Construction and Building Inspector

1. Construction and building inspectors examine the construction, alteration, or repair of buildings, highways and streets, sewer and water systems, dams, bridges, and other structures to ensure compliance with building codes and ordinances, zoning regulations, and contract specifications.
2. About 64,000 jobs; more than 50% work for local governments, primarily municipal or counting building departments.
3. Other; inspectors usually receive most of their training on the job, although some formal training is helpful. They need several years of experience as a manager, supervisor, or craft worker before becoming an inspector.
4. faster than average
5. The median income for construction and building inspectors is $32,300.

Cost Estimator

1. Cost estimators calculate cost of labor and materials needed to perform services or produce goods. On a large construction project, the estimator reviews the architect's drawings and specifications, visits the site, and gathers information to determine the quantity of materials and labor needed.
2. About 179,000 jobs; cost estimators work primarily in the construction industries.
3. associate degree/other: considerable experience as a construction craft worker or manager; also post-secondary education.

4. same as the average
5. entry-level income: between $17,000 and $21,000

Electrician

1. Electricians install, connect, test, and maintain electrical systems for climate control, security, and communication. A growing number of electricians install telephone and computer wiring and equipment.
2. About 528,000; more than half are employed in the construction industry. Others work as maintenance electricians and are employed in virtually every industry.
3. apprenticeship
4. slower than average
5. Median income: $29,850

Survey Technician

1. Survey technicians assist land surveyors by operating survey instruments and collecting information.
2. Surveyors, including survey technicians, hold about 96,000 jobs; more than 60% are employed by engineering, architectural, and surveying firms; another 25% are employed by the federal government.
3. associate degree
4. slower than average
5. median income: $27,000

Interior Designer

1. Interior designers plan the space and furnish the interiors of private homes, public buildings, and commercial establishments such as offices, restaurants, hospitals, hotels, and theaters.
2. About 301,000 (all designers); they usually work for design or architectural firms, department and home furnishing stores, or hotel and restaurant chains.
3. bachelor's degree
4. faster than average
5. median income: $30,680

CAREER ACTIVITY 10

Pilot

1. Pilots are highly-trained professionals who fly airplanes and helicopters to transport people and products, inspect pipelines, dust crops, and perform similar duties.
2. Civilian pilots hold about 90,000 jobs; 60% work for airlines. Many others are flight instructors.
3. associate degree/other: The armed forces have always been an important source of trained pilots for civilian jobs.
4. slower than average
5. median entry-level income for airline pilots at smaller airlines: $13,000; at larger airlines: $27,900

(continued next page)

Air Traffic Controller

1. Air traffic controllers rely on radar and visual observation to coordinate the movement of air traffic to make certain that planes stay a safe distance apart.
2. About 23,000; most work for the federal government, but some work for private air traffic control companies that provide service to non-FAA towers.
3. associate degree
4. same as average
5. entry-level income: $27,000

Aerospace Engineer

1. Aerospace engineers design, develop, test, and help manufacture commercial and military aircraft, missiles, and spacecraft.
2. About 56,000 jobs: about 50% work in aircraft and parts and guided missile and space vehicle manufacturing industries. Most work for government agencies.
3. bachelor's degree
4. slower than average
5. entry-level income: $30,860

Aircraft Mechanic

1. Aircraft mechanics perform scheduled maintenance, make repairs, and complete inspections required by the Federal Aviation Administration (FAA).
2. About 119,000; more than 60% work for airlines, nearly 20% work for aircraft assembly firms, and nearly 17% work for the federal government.
3. associate degree
4. same as average
5. entry-level income: $18,000 at smaller airlines; $28,200 at larger airlines

Aviation Safety Inspector

1. Aviation safety inspectors ensure that Federal Aviation Administration (FAA) regulations, which govern the quality and safety of aircraft equipment, aircraft operations, and personnel, are maintained. They also examine and certify aircraft pilots, pilot examiners, flight instructors, repair stations, schools, and instructional materials.
2. About 157,000 inspectors and compliance officers, which includes aviation safety inspectors; aviation safety inspectors work for the FAA.
3. associate degree/other: flight and maintenance training in the armed forces
4. same as the average
5. median income: $62,970

Precision Assembler

1. Precision assemblers must interpret detailed specifications and instructions and apply independent judgment to assemble products with a high degree of accuracy.

2. About 324,000; almost all of these jobs are in plants that manufacture durable goods.
3. other: technical school
4. slower than average
5. Information is somewhat limited; median income is approximately $17,260.

Reservation/Ticket Agent

1. Reservation agents work for airlines helping people plan trips and make reservations. They answer telephone inquiries, offer suggestions for travel arrangements, quote fairs, make and confirm reservations, and sell tickets.
2. About 139,000; more than 60% are employed by airlines. Others work for membership organizations such as automobile clubs and hotels.
3. other: formal company training programs; some college education
4. faster than average
5. median income: $21,160

Flight Attendant

1. Flight attendants see that all passengers have a safe, comfortable, enjoyable flight. Among other duties, they make sure the passenger cabin is in order, that supplies are adequate, and that emergency equipment is on board and functional.
2. About 105,000; commercial airlines employ the vast majority of all flight attendants.
3. other: high-school graduates; however, more and more attendants are college graduates
4. faster than average
5. entry-level income: $12,700

CAREER ACTIVITY 11

Marine Engineer

1. Marine engineers operate and maintain propulsion engines, boilers, generators, pumps, and other machinery on ships, tugboats, towboats, ferries, dredges, and research vessels.
2. About 7,600; about 45% of all water transportation workers work on board merchant marine ships or U.S. Navy ships.
3. other: engineering officers in the merchant marine must be licensed
4. same as average
5. median income: $30,940

Rail Engineer

1. Locomotive engineers and rail yard engineers operate locomotives in yards, stations, and over the track between distant stations and yards.
2. About 22,000 locomotive engineers and about 6,000 rail yard engineers; railroads employ about 82% of all rail transportation workers. The rest

(continued next page)

work for state and local governments and for mining and manufacturing establishments.

3. other: on-the-job training
4. slower than average
5. median income: from $47,700 to $63,900, depending on the train and type of service

Diesel Mechanic

1. Diesel mechanics repair and maintain diesel engines that power transportation equipment, construction equipment, and farm equipment.
2. About 250,000; nearly 25% service trucks and other diesel-powered equipment for customers of equipment dealers, leasing companies, and repair shops. More than 20% work for trucking companies. The rest work for public transit companies, school systems, and federal, state, and local governments.
3. associate degree or apprenticeship
4. same as average
5. median income: $30,400

Automotive Mechanic

1. Automotive mechanics repair and service automobiles and light trucks with gasoline engines.
2. About 736,000; the majority work for retail and wholesale automotive dealers, independent repair shops, and gasoline service stations.
3. associate degree
4. same as average
5. median income: $22,800

Customs Inspector

1. Customs inspectors enforce laws governing imports and exports. Stationed in the United States and overseas at airports, seaports, and border crossing points, they examine, count, weigh, gauge, measure, and sample commercial and noncommercial cargoes entering and leaving the United States to determine admissibility and the amount of duties that must be paid.
2. Inspectors and compliance officers, including customs inspectors, hold about 157,000 jobs. Federal, state, and local governments and the U.S. Postal Service employ most customs inspectors.
3. other: combination of on-the-job training and classroom instruction
4. same as average
5. median income: $39,050

CAREER ACTIVITY 12

Stationary Engineer

1. Stationary engineers operate and maintain systems that can include boilers, air-conditioning and refrigeration equipment, diesel engines, turbines,

generators, pumps, condensers, and compressors.
2. About 30,000; they work in a variety of places, including factories, hospitals, hotels, office and apartment buildings, schools, and shopping malls.
3. apprenticeship
4. slower than average
5. median income: $30,700

Water and Wastewater Treatment Plant Operator

1. Operators control processes and equipment to remove solid materials, chemical compounds, and microorganisms from water or to render them harmless. They also control pumps, valves, and other processing equipment to move the water or wastewater through the various treatment processes and dispose of the waste materials removed from the water.
2. About 95,000; the vast majority work for local governments; about half work as water treatment plant operators and the other half as wastewater treatment plant operators.
3. associate degree/other: on-the-job training with formal classroom or self-paced study programs; one-year certificate programs
4. slower than average
5. median income: $27,100

Nuclear Engineer

1. Nuclear engineers conduct research on nuclear energy and radiation. They design, develop, monitor, and operate nuclear power plants.
2. About 15,000; about 20% each work in utilities, the federal government, and engineering firms. Another 10% work in research and testing.
3. bachelor's degree
4. same as average
5. entry-level income: $33,600

Petroleum Engineer

1. Petroleum engineers explore for workable reservoirs containing oil or natural gas. When one is discovered, they work to achieve the maximum profitable recovery from the reservoir.
2. About 14,000; most petroleum engineers work in the petroleum industry and closely allied fields.
3. bachelor's degree
4. slower than average
5. entry-level income: $38,280 per year

Petroleum Technician

1. Petroleum technicians measure and record physical and geologic conditions in oil or gas wells using instruments lowered into wells or by analyzing mud from the wells. They collect and examine geological data or test geological samples to determine petroleum and mineral content.
2. Science technicians in general hold about 231,000

(continued next page)

jobs. Petroleum technicians work in the petroleum industry and closely allied fields.

3. associate degree
4. same as average
5. entry-level income for science technicians: $26,900; government positions: $14,900 to $18,700

Mobile Heavy Equipment Mechanic

1. Mobile heavy equipment mechanics perform routine maintenance on the diesel engines that power most heavy equipment. They repair, replace, clean, and lubricate parts as necessary and reassemble and test the engine for operating efficiency.
2. About 101,000; more than 50% work for mobile heavy equipment dealers and construction contractors. About 20% are employed by federal, state, and local governments.
3. associate degree/other: 1- to 2-year training programs leading to a certificate of completion
4. slower than average
5. median income: $28,800

CAREER ACTIVITY 13

Physician

1. Physicians diagnose illnesses and prescribe and administer treatment for people suffering from injury or disease. They also counsel patients on diet, hygiene, and preventive health care.
2. About 539,000; about 67% work in office-based practice, including clinics and HMOs. About 25% are employed in hospitals. Others practice in the federal government, or in public health clinics.
3. Other: It usually takes about 11 years to become a physician: 4 years of undergraduate school, 4 years of medical school, and 3 years in residency.
4. faster than average
5. median income: $156,000

Medical Scientist

1. Medical scientists work on basic research into normal biological systems to understand the causes of and to discover treatments for disease and other health problems.
2. About 118,000, not counting those who hold biology faculty positions in colleges and universities; about 6% work in research and testing laboratories, and most of the rest work in hospitals and the drug industries.
3. bachelor's degree
4. faster than average
5. entry-level income: $22,900

Biochemist
1. Biochemists study the chemical composition of living things. They try to understand the complex

chemical combinations and reactions involved in metabolism, reproduction, growth, and heredity.
2. About 118,000, not counting those who hold biology faculty positions in colleges and universities; about 6% work in research and testing laboratories, and most of the rest work in hospitals and the drug industries.
3. bachelor's degree
4. faster than average
5. entry-level income: $22,900

Medical Technologist

1. Medical technologists, also known as clinical laboratory technologists, perform complex chemical, biological, hematological, immunologic, microscopic, and bacteriological tests.
2. About 274,000 jobs; more than half work in hospitals. Most others work in medical laboratories or physicians' offices or clinics.
3. bachelor's degree
4. same as average
5. income ranges from $26,000 to $38,844 per year

Physical Therapist

1. Physical therapists improve mobility, relieve pain, and prevent or limit permanent physical disabilities of patients suffering from injuries or disease.
2. About 102,000; hospitals employ about 33%, and physical therapy offices employ about 25%. Others are self-employed in private practice, teach in academic institutions, or conduct research.
3. bachelor's degree
4. faster than average
5. median income (full-time): $37,600

Cardiovascular Technologist

1. Cardiovascular technologists assist physicians in diagnosing and treating cardiac (heart) and peripheral vascular (blood) ailments.
2. About 30,000; most cardiovascular technologists work in cardiologists' offices, cardiac rehabilitation centers, or health maintenance organizations.
3. associate degree
4. faster than average
5. median income: $32,000

Medical Records Technician

1. Medical records technicians organize and evaluate patient medical records for completeness and accuracy. When assembling a patient's medical record, they ensure that all forms are present and properly identified and signed, and that all necessary information is in a computer file. They consult a classification manual and assign a code to each diagnosis and procedure.
2. About 81,000; about 50% work in hospitals; most of the rest work in nursing homes, medical group

(continued next page)

practices, health maintenance organizations, and clinics.
3. associate degree
4. faster than average
5. median income: $36,700 (for accredited record technicians)

Licensed Practical Nurse

1. Licensed practical nurses (LPNs) provide basic bedside care for the sick, injured, convalescing, and handicapped, under the direction of physicians and registered nurses.
2. About 702,000; 40% work in hospitals, 25% in nursing homes, and more than 10% in doctors' offices and clinics. Others work for temporary help agencies, home health care services, or government agencies.
3. other: one-year practical nursing program, including classroom study and supervised clinical practice
4. faster than average
5. median income: $23,400

CAREER ACTIVITY 14

Biological Scientist

1. Biological scientists study living organisms and their relationship to their environment.
2. Almost 1 in 3 non-faculty biological scientists are employed by federal, state, and local governments. Most of the rest work in the drug industry or in research and testing laboratories.
3. bachelor's degree
4. faster than average
5. median entry-level income in private industry: $22,900

Geologist

1. Geologists study the physical aspects and history of the earth. They identify and examine rocks, study information collected by remote sensing instruments in satellites, conduct geological surveys, construct maps, and use instruments to measure the earth's gravity and magnetic field. They design and monitor waste disposal sites, preserve water supplies, reclaim contaminated land and water to comply with federal environmental regulations, and locate safe sites for hazardous waste facilities and landfills.
2. Geologists and geophysicists hold about 46,000 jobs; many more hold geology, geophysics, and oceanography faculty positions in colleges and universities. About 20% are employed in oil and gas companies, and many others work for consulting firms and business services, especially engineering services. Others work for the federal government or for nonprofit research institutions.

3. bachelor's degree
4. same as average
5. entry-level income: $27,900, but varies widely depending on the industry; petroleum, mineral, and mining industries offer higher income

Forester

1. Foresters manage forested lands for a variety of purposes. Those working in private industry may procure timber from private landowners. Foresters contact local forest owners and take inventory to the timber on the property, appraise the timber's worth, negotiate the purchase of timber, and draw up a contract for procurement. They determine how best to conserve wildlife habitats, creek beds, water quality, and soil stability and how best to comply with environmental regulations. They also supervise the planting and growing of new trees. Those who work for state and federal governments manage public forests and parks and also work with private landowners to protect and manage forest land outside of the public domain.
2. About 41,000 (including conservation scientists); about 60% work for federal, state, and local governments. The rest work in private industry, mainly in the forestry industry.
3. bachelor's degree
4. same as average
5. entry-level income (federal government and private sector): $18,700; generally lower in state and local governments.

Groundskeeper

1. Groundskeepers maintain a variety of facilities including athletic fields, golf courses, cemeteries, university campuses, and parks. They usually do many of the same tasks as maintenance personnel, but they typically have more extensive knowledge in horticulture, landscape design and construction, pest management, irrigation, and erosion control.
2. Groundskeepers and gardeners hold about 707,000; about 40% work for lawn and garden service companies. More than 10% each work for firms operating and building real estate and amusement and recreation facilities such as golf courses and race tracks. Others work for the government or for schools, hospitals, cemeteries, hotels, retail nurseries, or garden stores.
3. other: high-school diploma (required for some jobs)
4. same as average
5. median income: $14,900

Landscape Architect

1. Landscape architects design areas so that they are

(continued next page)

functional, beautiful, and compatible with the natural environment.

2. About 14,000; about 60% work for firms that provide landscape architecture services. Most of the rest work for architectural firms or the federal government.
3. bachelor's degree
4. same as average
5. median income in private sector: about $40,000; in federal government: about $48,000

Farm Operator

1. The specific tasks of farm operators are determined by the type of farm they operate. One crop farms, they are responsible for planning, tilling, planting, fertilizing, cultivating, spraying, and harvesting. On livestock, dairy, and poultry farms, they must plan, feed, and care for animals and keep barns, pens, coops, and other farm buildings clean and in repair. On horticultural specialty farms, they oversee production of ornamental plants, nursery products, and fruits and vegetables grown in greenhouses.
2. About 1,327,000; about 90% are self-employed farm operators.
3. associate degree
4. slower than average
5. Farm operators and managers who are paid a wage or income and work full-time have median income of $16,330.

CAREER ACTIVITY 15

Electrical and Electronics Engineer

1. Electrical and electronics engineers design, develop, test, and supervise the manufacture of electrical and electronic equipment, including radar, computer hardware, and communication and video equipment.
2. About 349,000; most jobs are in engineering and business consulting firms, manufacturers of electrical and electronic equipment, professional and scientific instruments, and government agencies.
3. bachelor's degree
4. same as average
5. entry-level income: $34,840

Electronic Equipment Repairer

1. Electronic equipment repairers install, maintain, and repair electronic equipment used in offices, factories, homes, hospitals, aircraft, and other places. They test, repair, and calibrate equipment to ensure that it functions properly.
2. Approximately 389,000; many work for telephone companies. Others work for electronic and transportation equipment manufacturers, machinery

and equipment wholesalers, hospitals, electronic repair shops, and maintenance firms.
3. other: 1 to 2 years of formal training; some apprenticeship programs are available
4. slower than average
5. median income: $30,800

Industrial Electronics Technician

1. Industrial electronic s technicians install and repair industrial controls, radar and missile control systems, medical diagnostic equipment, and communication equipment.
2. About 66,000; about 33% are employed by the federal government, almost all in the Department of Defense.
3. other: 1 to 2 years of formal training; some apprenticeship programs are available
4. slower than average in the federal government; faster than average in the private sector
5. median income: $30,800

Computer/Office Machine Service Technician

1. Computer and office machine repairers install equipment, do preventive maintenance, and correct problems on computers, peripheral equipment, photocopiers, cash registers, and mail processing equipment.
2. About 134,000; approximately 75,000 specialize in computer equipment, and the rest repair mainly office equipment. About 60% are employed by wholesalers of computers and office equipment; the rest work in retail establishments.
3. other: 1 to 2 years of formal training; some complete apprenticeship programs
4. faster than average
5. median income: $30,780

Electrician

1. Electricians install, connect, test, and maintain electrical systems for a variety of purposes, including climate control, security, and communication. A growing number of electricians install telephone and computer wiring and equipment.
2. About 528,000; more than half work in the construction industry. Others work as maintenance electricians and are employed in virtually every industry.
3. apprenticeship
4. slower than average
5. median income: $29,850

Electronic Semiconductor Processor

1. Electronic semiconductor processors process materials used in the manufacture of electronic semiconductors; load semiconductor material into furnaces; saw formed ingots into segments; load individual segments into crystal-growing

(continued next page)

chambers and monitor controls; locate crystal axes using x-ray equipment; and load wafers into a series of special-purpose furnaces, chemical baths, and equipment used to form circuitry and change conductive properties.
2. About 33,000; most work for electronic manufacturing firms or manufacturers of communication equipment.
3. other: on-the-job training
4. same as average
5. median income: $19,240

CAREER ACTIVITY 16

Tool Programmer

1. Tool programmers analyze blueprints, compute size and position of cuts, determine sequence of machine operations, select tools, and calculate the machine speed and feed rates. They then write the program in the language of the machine's controller and store it. A growing number of firms employ CAD systems to assist in writing programs.
2. About 376,000 machinists and tool programmers; most work in small machining shops or in manufacturing firms that produce durable goods.
3. apprenticeship/other: vocational school education or post-secondary education
4. slower than average
5. median income: $27,040

Machinist

1. Machinists use machine tools such as lathes, drill presses, and milling machines to produce precision metal parts. Increasingly, the machine tools are controlled by computer.
2. About 376,000 machinists and tool programmers; most work in small machining shops or in manufacturing firms that produce durable goods.
3. apprenticeship/other: vocational school education or post-secondary education
4. slower than average
5. median income: $27,040

Metal- and Plastics-Working Machine Operators

1. Manual and numerical control machine operators in the metalworking and plastics industries play a major role in producing most of the consumer products we rely on today. Metalworking and plastics-working machine operators are being called upon to work with CNC equipment.
2. About 1,445,000; of these, 75,000 are CNC operators. Most work in manufacturing industries.
3. other: on-the-job training
4. slower than average
5. median income: about $21,840

Tool and Die Makers

1. Tool and die makers are highly skilled workers who produce tools, dies, and special guiding and holding devices that are used in machines that cut, shape, and form metal and other materials to produce a variety of products. Firms commonly use CAD to develop products and CNC machines to produce dies.
2. About 142,000; most work in industries that manufacture metalworking machinery and equipment, motor vehicles, aircraft, and plastic products.
3. apprenticeship/other: informal on-the-job training combined with classroom instruction at a vocational school or two-year college
4. slower than average
5. median income: $34,320

CAREER ACTIVITY 17

Mechanical Engineer

1. Mechanical engineers plan and design tools, engines, machines, and other mechanical equipment. They design and develop power-using machines such as robots and industrial production equipment.
2. About 231,000; more than 60% are in manufacturing. Business and engineering consulting services and governmental agencies provided most of the remaining jobs.
3. bachelor's degree
4. same as average
5. entry-level income: $35,050

Mechanical Engineering Technician

1. Mechanical engineering technicians help engineers design, develop, test, and manufacture machinery, industrial robots, and other equipment.
2. Engineering technicians, which includes mechanical engineering technicians, hold about 685,000 jobs. About 40% work in manufacturing, and nearly 25% work in service industries.
3. associate degree
4. slower than average
5. median income (junior level): $16,590

Computer Programmer

1. Computer programmers write, test, and maintain the detailed constructions, call programs or software, that list in a logical order the steps that computers must execute to perform their functions.
2. About 573,000; they are employed in most industries, but the largest concentrations are in data processing service organizations.
3. bachelor's degree
4. same as average
5. median entry-level income in large companies:

(continued next page)

$33,000; in smaller companies: $29,500; in the federal government: $18,700

Precision Assembler

1. Precision assemblers must interpret detailed specifications and instructions and apply independent judgment to assemble products with a high degree of accuracy.
2. About 324,000; almost all of these jobs are in plants that manufacture durable goods.
3. other: technical school
4. slower than average
5. Information is somewhat limited; median income is approximately $17,260.

Industrial Electronics Technician

1. Industrial electronic s technicians install and repair industrial controls, radar and missile control systems, medical diagnostic equipment, and communication equipment.
2. About 66,000; about 33% are employed by the federal government, almost all in the Department of Defense.
3. other: 1 to 2 years of formal training; some apprenticeship programs are available
4. slower than average in the federal government; faster than average in the private sector
5. median income: $30,800

Military Communication and Intelligence Specialist

1. Communication and intelligence specialists serve as intelligence gatherers and interpreters, cryptologists, information analysts, translators, science and engineering researchers, and in related occupations.
2. The armed forces employ 119,392 communication and intelligence specialists.
3. other: high-school diploma; requirements for each branch of service vary
4. slower than average
5. entry-level income: $10,248 (enlisted); $19,260 (officer)

CAREER ACTIVITY 18

Survey Technician

1. Survey technicians assist land surveyors by operating survey instruments and collecting information. Many survey instruments are now laser-guided.
2. Surveyors, including survey technicians, hold about 96,000 jobs; more than 60% are employed by engineering, architectural, and surveying firms; another 25% are employed by the federal government.
3. associate degree
4. slower than average
5. median annual income: $27,000

Physician

1. Physicians diagnose illnesses and prescribe and administer treatment for people suffering from injury or disease. Increasingly, they are using laser devices to perform various forms of surgery, much of which can be performed in the physician's office or clinic.
2. About 539,000; about 67% work in office-based practice, including clinics and HMOs. About 25% are employed in hospitals. Others practice in the federal government, or in public health clinics.
3. Other: It usually takes about 11 years to become a physician: 4 years of undergraduate school, 4 years of medical school, and 3 years in residency.
4. faster than average
5. median income: $156,000

Aerospace Engineer

1. Aerospace engineers design, develop, test, and help manufacture commercial and military aircraft, missiles, and spacecraft. They develop new products, often involving laser and fiber optic technology, for use in areas such as guidance, navigation and control, instrumentation, and communication .
2. About 56,000 jobs: about 50% work in aircraft and parts and guided missile and space vehicle manufacturing industries. Most work for government agencies.
3. bachelor's degree
4. slower than average
5. entry-level income: $30,860

Communication Equipment Mechanic

1. Communication equipment mechanics, also known as telecommunications technicians, install, repair, and maintain complex and sophisticated telephone communication equipment. Increasingly, they are being trained to perform multiple tasks, ranging from splicing fiber optic cable, to programming switches, to installing telephones. Those who install and repair stationary and mobile radio transmitting and receiving equipment sometimes repair microwave and fiber optic installations.
2. About 118,000; most of them work for telephone companies.
3. other: 1 to 2 years of formal training in electronics
4. slower than average
5. median income: $28,180

Mechanical Engineering Technician

1. Mechanical engineering technicians help engineers design, develop, test, and manufacture machinery, industrial robots, and other equipment.
2. Engineering technicians, which includes mechanical engineering technicians, hold about 685,000

(continued next page)

TECHNOLOGY INTERACTIONS Teacher's Resource Guide

jobs. About 40% work in manufacturing, and nearly 25% work in service industries.
3. associate degree
4. slower than average
5. median income (junior level): $16,590

Military Electronic Equipment Repairers

1. Within the armed forces, electronic equipment repairers manage regular maintenance and repair of avionics, communication, radar, and air traffic control equipment.
2. The armed forces employ 221,353 electronic equipment repairers.
3. other: high-school diploma; requirements for each branch of service vary
4. slower than average
5. entry-level income: $10,248 (enlisted); $19,260 (officer)

CAREER ACTIVITY 19

Aerospace Engineer

1. Aerospace engineers design, develop, test, and help manufacture commercial and military aircraft, missiles, and spacecraft. They develop new products, often involving laser and fiber optic technology, for use in areas such as guidance, navigation and control, instrumentation, and communication.
2. About 56,000 jobs: about 50% work in aircraft and parts and guided missile and space vehicle manufacturing industries. Most work for government agencies.
3. bachelor's degree
4. slower than average
5. entry-level income: $30,860

Chemical Engineer

1. Chemical engineers apply the principles of chemistry and engineering to solve problems involving the production or use of chemicals.
2. About 50,000; manufacturing industries employ about 69%, primarily in the chemical, petroleum refining, or related industries.
3. bachelor's degree
4. same as average
5. entry-level income: $39,204

Civil Engineer

1. Civil engineers design and supervise the construction of roads, airports, tunnels, bridges, water supply and sewage systems, and buildings.
2. About 184,000; more than 40% are in federal, state, and local government agencies. Another 40% are in firms that provide engineering consulting services, and the construction industry, public utilities, transportation, and manufacturing industries account for most of the rest.

3. bachelor's degree
4. same as average
5. entry-level income: $29,809

Mechanical Engineer

1. Mechanical engineers plan and design tools, engines, machines, and other mechanical equipment.
2. About 231,000 jobs; more than 60% work in manufacturing. The rest work in business and engineering consulting services and government agencies.
3. bachelor's degree
4. same as average
5. Entry-level income: $35,000

Electrical and Electronics Engineer

1. Electrical and electronics engineers design, develop, test, and supervise the manufacture of electrical and electronic equipment, including radar, computer hardware, and communication and video equipment.
2. About 349,000; most jobs are in engineering and business consulting firms, manufacturers of electrical and electronic equipment, professional and scientific instruments, and government agencies.
3. bachelor's degree
4. same as average
5. entry-level income: $34,840

Metallurgical, Ceramic, and Materials Engineer

1. Metallurgical, ceramic, and materials engineers develop new types of metal alloys, ceramics, composites, and other materials to meet special requirements. Most metallurgical engineers work in one of three branches of metallurgy: extractive or chemical, physical, and mechanical or process.
2. Approximately 19,000; more than 25% work in metal-producing industries.
3. bachelor's degree
4. slower than average
5. entry-level income: $33,429

Nuclear Engineer

1. Nuclear engineers conduct research on nuclear energy and radiation. They design, develop, monitor, and operate nuclear power plants.
2. About 15,000; about 20% each work in utilities, the federal government, and engineering firms. Another 10% work in research and testing.
3. bachelor's degree
4. same as average
5. entry-level income: $33,600

Computer Engineer

1. Computer engineers generally design computers and conduct research to improve their design or use for particular purposes.

(continued next page)

2. About 828,000; although they are found in most industries, the greatest concentration of jobs is in the computer and data processing services industries. Many others work for government agencies, computer manufacturers, insurance companies, and universities.
3. bachelor's degree
4. faster than average
5. median income: $44,000

CAREER ACTIVITY 20

Physicist

1. Physicists explore and identify basic principles governing the structure and behavior of matter, the generation and transfer of energy, and the interaction of matter and energy. Some use these principles in theoretical areas; others apply their knowledge to practical areas such as the development of advanced materials, electronic and optical devices, and medical equipment.
2. About 20,000; about 25% of all non-faculty physicists and astronomers work in research. The federal government employs almost 20%. Others work in colleges and universities in non-faculty positions or for state governments, electrical and electronic equipment manufacturers, drug companies, and search and navigation equipment manufacturers.
3. other: doctoral degree is the usual requirement
4. slower than average
5. median income: $64,000 (civilian); $67,240 (government)

Geophysicist

1. Geophysicists and geologists use the principles of physics and mathematics to study the physical aspects and history of the earth.
2. Geologists and geophysicists hold about 46,000 jobs; many more hold geology, geophysics, and oceanography faculty positions in colleges and universities. About 20% are employed in oil and gas companies, and many others work for consulting firms and business services, especially engineering services. Others work for the federal government or for nonprofit research institutions.
3. bachelor's degree
4. same as average
5. entry-level income: $27,900, but varies widely depending on the industry; petroleum, mineral, and mining industries offer higher income.

Astronomer

1. Astronomers use the principles of physics and mathematics to learn about the fundamental nature of the universe, including the sun, moon, planets, stars, and galaxies. They also apply their knowledge to problems in navigation and space flight.
2. Physicists and astronomers hold about 20,000 jobs; in addition, a significant number hold physics faculty positions at college and universities. About 25% of all non-faculty physicists and astronomers work in research. The federal government employs almost 20%. Others work in colleges and universities in non-faculty positions or for state governments, electrical and electronic equipment manufacturers, drug companies, and search and navigation equipment manufacturers.
3. other: doctoral degree is the usual requirement
4. slower than average
5. median income: $64,000 (civilian); $67,240 (government)

College and University Faculty

1. College and university faculty teach and advise college students and perform a significant part of the nation's research.
2. About 823,000; mostly in public institutions
3. other: doctoral degree
4. same as average
5. median income: $49,500

Nuclear Engineer

1. Nuclear engineers conduct research on nuclear energy and radiation. They design, develop, monitor, and operate nuclear power plants.
2. About 15,000; about 20% each work in utilities, the federal government, and engineering firms. Another 10% work in research and testing.
3. bachelor's degree
4. same as average
5. entry-level income: $33,600

Nuclear Science Technician

1. Science technicians use the principles and theories of science and mathematics to solve problems in research and development and to help invent and improve products. Their jobs are more practically oriented than those of scientists. Nuclear technicians operate nuclear test and research equipment, monitor radiation, and assist nuclear engineers and physicists in research.
2. Science technicians hold about 231,000 jobs; over 33% work in manufacturing, mostly in the chemical industry, but also in food processing. About 15% work in education services and another 15% work in research and development.
3. associate degree
4. same as average
5. median income (science technicians): $26,900

Answer Key for Chapter Reviews

CHAPTER 1

1. Industrial
2. system
3. feedback
4. tool
5. Resources
6. computer integrated manufacturing
7. process
8. subsystems
9. output
10. Bio-related
11. c
12. a
13. d
14. a
15. b
16. b
17. c
18. a
19. d
20. d

CHAPTER 2

1. invention
2. ergonomics
3. sketching
4. brainstorming
5. appearance
6. design
7. innovation
8. prototype
9. design brief
10. rendering
11. c
13. d
12. c
14. b
15. a
16. d
17. b
18. a
19. b
20. c

CHAPTER 3

1. prototypes
2. Cartesian
3. drafting
4. CPU

5. puck
6. read-only
7. library
8. CD-ROM
9. CAM
10. digitizer
11. solid model

```
O Y C R I W E R C N B E
C P R O T O T Y P E S U
F A D S E V M P U C K R
A D R I O J E S S A D T
X I A T V F Q B L T W I
S U F R E A D O N L Y Z
E D T C S S E C T I B N
M W I F O H I C D B T Y
E S N G L I T A V R C K
Q U G L I X S M N A R O J
T O T M D T C D E R Y M
T H I D M O I W R Y E N
A C F L O C U Z T R I L
W A O K D E A G E M J E
D O R H E X O O S R E T
A R D I L E W U R H T O
```

12. d
13. a
14. b
15. a
16. d
17. c
18. b
19. b
20. a

CHAPTER 4

Down

1. desktop publishing
2. digital
6. folio
7. line art

Across

3. leading
4. pica

(continued next page)

5. crop
8. publishing
9. scanner
11. page layout
11. c
12. b
13. a
14. a
15. d
16. c
17. c
18. a
19. b
20. d

CHAPTER 5
1. storyboard
2. cel
3. model
4. Persistence of vision
5. key frames
6. primitives
7. flip-book
8. frame
9. Exposure sheets
10. claymation
11. b
12. a
13. c
14. c
15. b
16. false
17. true
18. false
19. false
20. true

CHAPTER 6
Down

2. resource
3. domain
4. hypertext
5. e-mail
6. hyperlinks
8. modem

Across

1. browser
6. home page
7. network
9. communication
11. d
12. c
13. a
14. a
15. b

16. c
17. b
18. d
19. a
20. c

CHAPTER 7
1. very high frequency (VHF)
2. Multimedia
3. audio
4. Amplitude modulation (AM)
5. Sound
6. Video
7. ultra high frequency (UHF)
8. hypermedia
9. frequency modulation (FM)
10. wavelength
11. a
12. d
13. b
14. b
15. F
16. T
17. T
18. T
19. F
20. F

CHAPTER 8
Down

1. prototype
2. manufacturing
3. industrial
4. custom
5. secondary

Across

1. primary
4. continuous
6. CAD/CAM
7. raw
8. job lot

11. design and engineering
12. purchasing
13. production
14. d
15. a
16. c
17. a
18. b
19. c
20. d

CHAPTER 9
1.superstructure

(continued next page)

2. zoning
3. specifications
4. building codes
5. foundation
6. force
7. smart buildings
8. load
9. structural member
10. plans

Puzzle solution: Before designing a structure, you must understand its intended use.

NOTE: Accept answers to 11 through 14 in any order.
11. inputs
12. processes
13. outputs
14. feedback
15. C
16. D
17. A
18. A
19. D
20. B

CHAPTER 10

1. Inertia
2. fluid
3. Aerospace
4. friction
5. ailerons
6. drag
7. Bernoulli
8. airfoil
9. Aerodynamics
10. force
11. Gravity

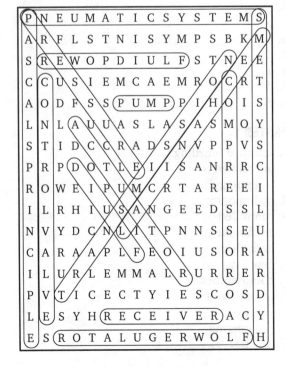

12. a
13. c
14. c
15. a

16. c
17. b
18. d
19. a
20. a

CHAPTER 11

1. transportation
2. buoyancy
3. diesel engine
4. maglev
5. gasoline piston engine
6. vessel

Puzzle solution: Joshua Slocum, the first person to sail alone around the world (1895-1898), could not swim.
7. b
8. a
9. d
10. d
11. c
12. c
13. d
14. a
15. c
16. d
17. a
18. b
19. c
20. b

CHAPTER 12

1. pneumatic systems
2. mechanical advantage

(continued next page)

8. c
9. d
10. b
11. a
12. c
13. c
14. b
15. d
16. b
17. a
18. e
19. a
20. fluid, compressor or pump, reservoir or receiver, control valves, actuators, flow regulators, transmission lines

CHAPTER 13

Down

2. immunization
6. genetic

Across

1. diagnosis
3. human factors
4. biomechanical
5. ergonomics
7. prosthesis
8. c
9. d
10. d
11. a
12. c
13. c
14. a
15. b
16. b
17. d
18. a
19. d
20. c

CHAPTER 14

1. selective breeding
2. bio-related technology
3. hydroponics
4. controlled environment agriculture
5. heredity
6. photosynthesis
7. chromosome
8. genetic engineering
9. genetics

10. bioprocessing
11. b
12. c
13. a
14. b
15. a
16. d
17. a
18. d
19. d
20. clearing the soil, tilling the soil, planting the seeds, cultivating the crops, harvesting the crops.

CHAPTER 15

1. circuit
2. potential difference
3. electricity
4. resistance
5. battery
6. current
7. transistor
8. Ohm's law
9. generator
10. electromagnetism
11. a
12. c
13. c
14. b
15. b
16. d
17. d
18. b
19. a
20. d

CHAPTER 16

1. computer numerical control
2. computer-aided manufacturing
3. computer-aided design
4. Cartesian coordinates
5. simulation software
6. flexible manufacturing system
7. CAD/CAM
8. c
9. c
10. d
11. d
12. b
13. a
14. d
15. d
16. c
17. a
18. b
19. d
20. b

(continued next page)

TECHNOLOGY INTERACTIONS Teacher's Resource Guide
Copyright © Glencoe/McGraw-Hill

CHAPTER 17

1. robot
2. automation
3. degree of freedom
4. robotics
5. feedback control
6. work envelope
7. control system
8. scanner, sensor
9. manipulators
10. pneumatic, hydraulic
11. lead-through programming
12. automation
13. d
14. a
15. b
16. d
17. c
18. a
19. b
20. d

CHAPTER 18

Down

1. directional light
2. electromagnetic wave
3. monochromatic light
6. coherent light

Across

4. photon
5. holography
7. laser
8. c
9. d
10. a
11. c
12. b
13. b
14. c
15. d
16. b
17. a
18. c
19. d
20. b

CHAPTER 19

1. engineering
2. engineering process
3. standards
4. engineer
5. d
6. a
7. b
8. c
9. a
10. b.
11. b
12. d
13. b
14. c
15. a
16. c
17. c
18. a
19. d
20. d

CHAPTER 20

1. applied physics
2. work
3. machine
4. gravity
5. friction
6. mechanical advantage
7. force
8. power
9. inertia

Puzzle solution: James Clerk Maxwell (1831-1879), a brilliant physicist, described electromagnetic waves 20 years before anyone actually observed them. Maxwell often worked out his ideas by having imaginary scientific conversations with his dog, Tobi.

10. d
11. b
12. e
13. c
14. b
15. a
16. a
17. d
18. b
19. c
20. c

Answer Key for Chapter Tests

Answers to the short-answer questions in these chapter tests are brief and are intended as guidelines only. Student answers may vary. Encourage students to think beyond the information presented in the text.

CHAPTER 1

1. d
2. c
3. g
4. j
5. e
6. b
7. k
8. i
9. f
10. a
11. TRUE
12. TRUE
13. FALSE
14. TRUE
15. FALSE
16. the need to process raw materials to make them usable
17. The needs of the people change over time, creating a need and therefore the development of new systems and new technologies.
18. Electronics have improved all technologies by making them faster and more reliable.
19. All technologies rely on the same seven basic resources: people information, materials, energy, tools and machines, capital (money), and time.
20. Accept all reasonable responses; students should include the input, process, output, and feedback portions of the system in their explanation.

CHAPTER 2

1. b
2. h
3. a
4. k
5. d
6. i
7. c
8. j
9. g
10. e
11. FALSE
12. TRUE
13. TRUE
14. TRUE
15. FALSE
16. (1) Identify the need for a new design. (2) Gather as much information as possible about the need so that you can form ideas about how to meet it. (3) Develop alternative solutions. (4) Choose the best solution. (5) Implement the solution. (6) Evaluate the effectiveness of the solution.
17. People use problem solving skills whenever they make a decision, although they often do not realize it when the decision is an easy one.
18. Problem solving is an important part of the design process. It helps the designer arrive at the best solution to a design problem by organizing the designer's approach to the problem in a logical manner.
19. Probably the best way to test this type of design is to field-test it using a limited number of children. Note, however, that items for young children must meet rigid safety standards. You may wish to give students extra credit if they mention or address this need.
20. Two-dimensional models such as sketches can be created more quickly and with less effort than 3D models. In some cases, designers must demonstrate the worth of the design to an employer or client before a 3D model will be approved.

CHAPTER 3

1. e
2. g
3. d
4. a
5. j
6. b
7. i
8. l
9. k
10. c
11. d
12. c
13. b
14. Digitizers are used to help convert paper drawings into electronic CAD files. The mouse cannot be used to do this. You might prefer the mouse when you need to create a simple drawing quickly on a computer that is used for other purposes besides CAD.
15. CAD systems allow you to create a drawing once, then print or plot as many originals as you need.

(continued next page)

You can also make complex changes to a CAD drawing without having to redraw the entire drawing. CAD drawings can be stored on electronic media, saving much archival space.

16. CAD software is a tool that a skilled drafter can use to create drafted documents more quickly and accurately. However, the drafter must understand the basic concepts of drafting. CAD software cannot guarantee that a new design will be a good one or that the drawing contains all of the elements needed to describe an object completely. Only the drafter can do these things.

17. Architects: construction drawings; civil engineers: draw plans for new roads and bridges; electronic engineers: show the circuits for electronic devices such as computer systems and stereos. In CAD/CAM, CAD drawings are used to drive CNC machines to manufacture parts.   18.   I n addition to the CAD software, many CAD systems have additional hardware, such as a digitizer and puck, that are not found in non-CAD systems. They are also more likely to have large storage capacities, larger amounts of RAM, and larger monitors than non-CAD systems.

19. (–8,2), (4,2), (4,10), (–8,10) (in this order)

20. Students should realize that the larger the monitor is, the more detail they can see at one time, even when they have zoomed in on a specific area of the drawing.

CHAPTER 4

1. a
2. c
3. f
4. g
5. j
6. k
7. e
8. i
9. h
10. d
11. sans serif
12. type styles
13. photographs
14. process
15. folio
16. Both software and hardware are needed for desktop publishing depend on the complexity of the documents to be prepared. Software usually includes page layout software, word processor, drawing program, image editing program, and clip art or other electronic art sources. Hardware includes a computer with a powerful processor, enough RAM to run the programs, a CD-ROM drive, and possibly a scanner and digital camera.

17. You should include the kind and size of type to be used for text and headlines; the kinds of graphics you will use; whether you will use color; and what else you can do to encourage people to read the document.

18. Both leading and line length affect readability. Lies set too close or too far apart are difficult to read. Line length should be proportional to type size, because long lines of small type and short lines of large type are difficult to read.

19. Serif—body or main text of document; sans serif—headlines and headings; decorative—used sparingly to capture attention.

20. Scanners create digital images of photographs and other graphics that already exist. Digital cameras work just like regular cameras, except that they store the images electronically in a format that the computer can use.

CHAPTER 5

1. e
2. e
3. k
4. b
5. i
6. a
7. j
8. c
9. f
10. g
11. hand-drawn animation
12. model animation
13. computer animation
14. Storyboards are a series of rough sketches that guide each step of the film's production; exposure sheets are developed after the storyboard is complete and specify the number of frames needed for each word of dialogue.
15. Shading adds color and depth to the images and objects and allows the artist to simulate various types of materials.
16. Shading and lighting are used to make a scene more realistic by adding colors, textures, and highlights. Rendering is the process in which the computer combines information about shading and lighting with information about the models and animation to create the final animation sequence.
17. Key frames speed up the animation process by allowing only the first and last frames to be specified. The computer creates all the images in between.
18. Models are created either by changing and combining basic geometric shapes called *primitives* or by drawing free-form shapes.
19. Layout, design, and timing skills. Layout and design skills are necessary to create an interesting,

(continued next page)

coherent finished product. Without timing skills, the animation will not have the smooth flow that makes animation believable.

20. Answers may include cartoons, commercials, live-action films, and video and computer games.

CHAPTER 6

1. e
2. g
3. b
4. h
5. c
6. k
7. d
8. f
9. j
10. i
11. computer, modem, telephone line, communication software, and Internet service provider
12. Students should realize that not everyone who uses the Internet does so with good intentions.
13. Netiquette is polite behavior on the Internet. Examples will vary, but may include not "shouting" (typing in all capital letters) and avoiding the use of foul or inappropriate language.
14. A hyperlink is a software link that allows you to go directly from one Web site or page to another. Examples will vary, but may include links to NASA, various space missions, types of spacecraft, and history of space travel.
15. the mailbox, domain, and zone
16. (any three) .com—commercial firms and on-line services; .gov—government offices; .edu—educational organizations; .mil—military; .net—networks; .org—nonprofit organizations
17. The Internet is a huge, international network that contains within it many smaller, individual networks belonging to governments, commercial firms, educational institutions, and individuals.
18. "Traffic" (number of users) on the Internet and the number of people accessing a particular site at one time can slow communication considerably.
19. to avoid incurring long-distance charges while using the Internet
20. Students should demonstrate that they understand the issues: the convenience and huge information database of the Internet will make it increasingly popular. However, even though the Internet gives access to a tremendous amount of information, there are still many reasons for public libraries. For example, libraries have librarians who are skilled in helping people find information quickly.

CHAPTER 7

1. j
2. a
3. d
4. b
5. k
6. f
7. i
8. e
9. g
10. h
11. over-the-air broadcast, satellite, cable systems
12. Sound is a form of energy produced by vibrations that act on the ear so that we can hear. When sound waves reach our ears, they make our eardrums vibrate, causing us to hear the sound.
13. Multimedia is a combination of several kinds of communication, such as text, pictures, sound, video, and animation, in a single product.
14. Multimedia is used in video games, educational products, video-on-demand, etc. An example of a future use might be multimedia theaters in which the seats are wired to provide sensory input as the screen provides visual input.
15. Both radio and television deliver information and entertainment; however, radio is strictly an audio system; television combines audio and video.
16. A message is changed to a signal that is transmitted over a channel. The channel can be either the atmosphere or a cable. A receiver changes the signal back into audio and/or video information.
17. entertainment, distance learning, information (news), video conferencing, etc.
18. The lens of the camera collects light from the scene being televised. Mirrors separate the image into blue, red, and green images. Sensors create an electronic signal for each color; the signals are amplified and sent to an encoder, which combines the signals. The video and audio signals are sent to the transmitter, which produces the broadcast signal.
19. hypertext and hotspots
20. CD-ROM video is not currently as good as video-tape video because hardware is not yet capable of producing high-enough quality video in real time. This will probably change in the near future, as computers become faster and more powerful.

CHAPTER 8

1. g
2. k
3. i
4. a
5. c
6. h
7. b
8. j
9. d

(continued next page)

TECHNOLOGY INTERACTIONS Teacher's Resource Guide
Copyright © Glencoe/McGraw-Hill

10. f
11. alloy
12. thermoset
13. forming
14. Shearing
15. conditioning
16. Natural materials are those that occur in nature. Synthetic materials are made by people.
17. Ceramics are synthetic materials that are made by firing clay, sand, and other natural substances at very high temperatures.
18. Industrial materials are raw materials that have been processed to become products that can be used to make products.
19. In stamping, sheet metal is squeezed between dies to give it shape. In extrusion, the material is pushed, rather than squeezed, into shape, and the opening in the die determines its shape.
20. thermal (hardening, tempering, annealing); chemical (vulcanization); and mechanical (forging)

CHAPTER 9
1. b
2. c
3. i
4. g
5. d
6. k
7. j
8. a
9. f
10. e
11. FALSE
12. TRUE
13. FALSE
14. TRUE
15. FALSE
16. Tension is an internal force that pulls a material, and compression is an internal force that pushes a material.
17. Many structural shapes include triangles because they are strong and stable. Examples may include towers, domes, and structural members such as trusses.
18. A static load changes little, if at all; a dynamic load changes continuously.
19. Studs, joists, and rafters are structural members that help frame a house. Studs are upright members that give shape to the walls; joists are horizontal members that help form floors and ceilings. Rafters often help shape the roof.
20. trusses

CHAPTER 10
1. f

2. a
3. j
4. e
5. h
6. d
7. i
8. b
9. k
10. c
11. A body will remain at rest unless a force acts on it.
12. The change of motion is proportional to the force acting on the body.
13. For every action, there is an equal and opposite reaction.
14. Both are airfoils; the purpose of both is to direct air in such a way as to provide lift.
15. by making air move more smoothly over its surface.
16. They suck air into the front, compress and heat it, and then eject it from the back at high speed.
17. The greater the mass, the more gravitational pull is exerted on it.
18. They are curved more on top than on bottom; this helps create lift by reducing air pressure above the wing.
19. by changing the pitch of the blade
20. Ailerons make the plane roll from side to side; elevators make it climb and dive; rudder turns right or left.

CHAPTER 11
1. g
2. b
3. a
4. f
5. c
6. e
7. TRUE
8. FALSE
9. TRUE
10. FALSE
11. TRUE
12. TRUE
13. TRUE
14. FALSE
15. TRUE
16. The cost of air travel is increasing, and trains are traveling faster.
17. During the intake stroke, a diesel engine injects only air into the cylinder. A gasoline engine pumps in a mixture of gasoline and air. During the compression stroke, the compressed air in the diesel engine becomes hotter than the mixture in the gasoline engine. When the diesel fuel is sprayed into the cylinder, the hot air ignites it. A spark plug is used to ignite the compressed air/fuel mixture

(continued next page)

in a gasoline engine.

18. A boat floats when the weight of the water it displaces is equal to or greater than the weight of the boat.
19. 60 mph
20. Encourage students to adapt their arguments for or against a maglev system to their own area. Arguments in favor: speed of travel, less maintenance, reduced pollution, and less motor vehicle traffic. Arguments against: the high cost of construction, inability to utilize top speeds, and increased pollution from electric power plants.

CHAPTER 12

1. b
2. f
3. c
4. g
5. a
6. e
7. h
8. c
9. b
10. a
11. a
12. If fluids couldn't move, they would have no power.
13. Gas molecules have space between them. The molecules of solids and liquids do not.
14. fluid—material that is put under pressure to perform tasks; compressor or pump—supplies fluid under pressure to the system; reservoir or receiver—stores fluid and releases it as needed; control valves—open and close passages to direct fluid to proper location; actuators—change pressure into mechanical motion; flow regulators—control the speed of piston travel in a cylinder; transmission lines—pressurized fluid moves through these to various other components in the system.
15. A pump moves liquids. A bicycle pump compresses and moves air.
16. P
17. H
18. H
19. P
20. H

CHAPTER 13

1. c
2. e
3. h
4. b
5. d
6. a
7. g
8. TRUE

9. FALSE
10. FALSE
11. TRUE
12. TRUE
13. FALSE
14. TRUE
15. Design of prostheses to replace joints, tissues, organs, and organ systems; of machines that can monitor and measure bodily functions; helpful drugs; artificial systems to enhance senses; applying ergonomic principles in the design of equipment, devices, and environments.
16. Answers may relate to designing prostheses.
17. Information resources and material resources; information resources help health workers keep up with the latest developments in biology, chemistry, science, and engineering and encourage new discoveries. Material resources are important because physical enhancements must not be harmful to the human body and must be accepted by it.
18. Doctors can measure body temperature, blood pressure, pulse rate, breathing rate, blood chemicals, and electrical waves; tools such as the CAT scan that can provide highly detailed information.
19. Answers should include progress in the use of electronics and genetic engineering.
20. Things to be considered may include the height of the seated person, the person's reach and grasping abilities, the space required for maneuvering the wheelchair, and any other factors that relate to the strengths and limitations of the person.

CHAPTER 14

1. d
2. b
3. e
4. a
5. g
6. f
7. k
8. j
9. c
10. h
11. FALSE
12. TRUE
13. FALSE
14. FALSE
15. TRUE
16. Work can be done more easily and quickly. Some activities can be combined into one operation.
17. In vegetative propagation, plants can be created using cuttings of roots, stems, or leaves.
18. Bioprocessing is a natural way to clean up and maintain a good environment. Some algae can rid water of harmful pollutants such as oil. Microor-

(continued next page)

ganisms are used in sewage treatment plants.

19. 33

20. Possible positive responses include: long-distance space travel will not be possible if food cannot be grown in the space vehicle. Growing crops in space helps us learn more about CEA techniques that can be used on Earth. Negative responses may include: growing crops in space is expensive.

CHAPTER 15

1. j
2. i
3. e
4. f
5. b
6. a
7. h
8. d
9. g
10. k
11. TRUE
12. TRUE
13. FALSE
14. FALSE
15. Voltage is an excess of electrons that are stored. When applied to a conductor, the excess electrons move to where there are too few electrons. This flow of electrons through a conductor is current. Resistance is the opposition to the flow.
16. (a) When voltage is applied to a conductor, the current that moves through the conductor is directly proportional to the applied voltage; (b) $I = E/R$; (c) 6 amps; (d) $R = E/I$
17. (a) Components in a series circuit are connected one after another. Components in a parallel circuit are arranged in separate branches. (b) Student drawings should show a parallel circuit with at least two branches and a lightbulb in each.
18. Electricity is the control of voltage levels and the flow of current. Electronics is the control of the flow of electrons.
19. The result would be a much larger output current.
20. Input: electricity; process: conversion of radio waves to sound waves; output: the sound that is heard. Feedback may be available in the form of comments from listeners.

CHAPTER 16

1. g
2. a
3. h
4. c
5. f
6. b
7. d

8. TRUE
9. FALSE
10. TRUE
11. FALSE
12. TRUE
13. TRUE
14. FALSE
15. FALSE
16. (a) computer-aided design; (b) computer-aided manufacturing; (c)computer numerical control; (d) flexible manufacturing system; (e) manual data input
17. X2 and Z3
18. It saves time; manufacturers can go directly from the design and testing to the making of a product; the need for drawings and program writing is reduced; communication is increased within the company.
19. CAD: design the product; CAM: manufacture the product; CNC, MDI, and FMS are used in the manufacturing process.
20. a computer

CHAPTER 17

1. a
2. e
3. c
4. g
5. d
6. f
7. TRUE
8. FALSE
9. TRUE
10. TRUE
11. FALSE
12. FALSE
13. TRUE
14. Mobility, soil/rock/atmosphere testing capability, optical sensors, independent power system such as a solar system to recharge batteries, or sonar.
15. Hollerith had developed an electrical scanner and sensor. Modern robots must be able to gather data and provide feedback to a computer. They use various types of scanners and sensors to do this.
16. Human brains send commands to parts of the body and receive messages from the senses; computers send instructions to a robot and receive feedback from sensors.
17. Different motors may be used to control different joints. When motors receive an electrical signal, they move a small amount or step.
18. 38,772.72 cubic inches
19. The creation of instructions by guiding the robotic arm through a sequence of motions and programming the computer to remember the pattern of mo-

(continued next page)

tion; lead-through programming may be easier and faster than writing long, detailed programs.

20. The two major types of sensors are contact and non-contact. A camera is a non-contact sensor.

CHAPTER 18

1. c
2. a
3. f
4. b
5. g
6. h
7. d
8. TRUE
9. FALSE
10. FALSE
11. TRUE
12. FALSE
13. TRUE
14. FALSE
15. TRUE
16. Laser light is monochromatic, while ordinary light is made up of many colors. Laser light is directional; it spreads out very little compared with ordinary light. Laser light is coherent; all its waves are the same length and in phase.   17.   eyes (skin is also acceptable)
18. The excitation system produces energy. In the active medium, the energy is changed to light and amplified. The feedback mechanism consists of mirrors placed at either end of the active medium to build the strength of the laser beam. One mirror allows some of the light to escape as a laser beam.
19. In holograms, the images are three-dimensional. Answers should include being able to study images from various angles, such as plants and animals in science; equipment, vehicles, structures; in technology education; sculptures in art; etc.
20. Communication: fiber-optic systems and holography; manufacturing: many types of material processing and for measurement; construction: tasks involving straight lines or level surfaces.

CHAPTER 19

1. b
2. e
3. a
4. c
5. (1) Identify the need; (2) gather information; (3) develop alternative solutions; (4) select the best solution; (5) implement the solution; (6) evaluate the solution.
6. Answers should identify in order what is done at each step of the engineering process as it would apply to the clipboard design.

7. Students should identify the work done in the chosen occupation and tell why their interests and talents would make that occupation suitable to them.
8. b, d
9. m
10. i
11. h
12. k
13. a
14. b
15. f
16. l
17. j
18. e
19. c, k
20. g

CHAPTER 20

1. g
2. f
3. c
4. e
5. b
6. a
7. h
8. d
9. j
10. FALSE
11. TRUE
12. FALSE
13. TRUE
14. TRUE
15. FALSE
16. (1) State the problem; (2) gather information; (3) form a hypothesis; (4) perform experiments to test the hypothesis; (5) record and analyze data; (6) state the conclusion
17. An unbalanced force was applied to the ball to propel it through the air. Fluid friction between the air and the ball slow the ball. The force of gravity pulls it down to the Earth. When the ball hits the ground, surface friction slows, and finally causes it to stop.
18. First law—an object at rest will stay at rest and an object in motion will stay in motion; second law—the rate at which an object moves depends on the size of the unbalanced force acting on it and the mass of the object; third law—for every action there is an equal and opposite reaction.
19. A lever; students will probably say that this is because force is applied downward at one end to raise the object (overcome the force of gravity on the object—its weight) at the other end.
20. A flashlight, because space is a vacuum, and sound waves cannot travel through it.